SO SUE ME

SECRETS to BLOGGING, FASHION & BEAUTY

by Suzanne Jackson

BLACKWATER PRESS

First published in Ireland in 2013

Blackwater Press Ltd.

1–5 North Frederick Street, Dublin 1

Design, Layout and Cover: Liz White Designs

© Suzanne Jackson, 2013

ISBN: 978-0-9576170-8-7

The author and publisher gratefully acknowledge the following for permission to reproduce photographs: iStockphoto.com, Alamy Images, Evan Doherty, Colin Mulcahy, Nadia Power and Max Straeten.

The author and publisher wish to thank Evan Doherty Photography (https://www.facebook.com/evandohertyphotography), Tara O'Farrell Makeup (http://tara-makeup.com/), Sheena O'Brien Makeup (https://www.facebook.com/sheenamakeup), Nadine Walsh at House of Colour, Barry Finnegan at MorganBHair, Only (http://only.com/) and Starla (http://www.starla.ie/) for their assistance with shooting and styling many of the looks featured in this publication.

Printed in the Republic of Ireland

Contents

Acknowledgements

To my Mum and Dad – you have both taught me almost everything I know. You are truly amazing parents and still to this day strict on simple manners (haha), which has paid off throughout my journey. I love you both so much, you always put your children first and I am the luckiest daughter alive to have you both as my role models!

To my Publisher John O'Connor – thank you with all of my heart for making my dream a reality. You are a true gentleman and I enjoyed all those evening meetings over tea. Tea and chats warm my soul – and I could listen to your stories all night! Thanks also to the editorial team at Blackwater Press and Liz White, my designer.

Tara King – my back bone in this book! Thank you so much for all your time, ideas, opinions and advice! Without you this book just wouldn't be possible.

Dylan – my boyfriend, you are the best person I know! You are my rock and I love you very much! Thank you for putting up with me throughout my stressful times and enjoying the success of my happy times!

Sara and Róisin – you're both my sounding board, and true friends!

To my SoSueMe.ie contributors – Dave, Sam and Michelle – none of this would be possible without you guys! I'm so happy to call you my friends and I love the fact that you have grown with me and SoSueMe! I appreciate your time and I will forever cherish your support and encouragement! Go team SoSueMe!

To my book contributors, Evan Doherty – you are the most talented photographer I know! Thank you for the beautiful pictures and for putting up with my demands, haha! Happy to call you my friend and love working with you! Tara O'Farrell, you are a true talent! You are effortless at applying makeup and one I call the best. Same to you, Sheena O'Brien, you apply makeup as if you are colouring in effortlessly and the results are always 10/10! Thank you to Barry Finnegan and Nadine Walsh – the best hairdressers I know!

To my sister Carla – we fight a lot, but I love you underneath it all! We are probably just too alike! Keep the head up – you're beautiful inside and out!

To my old boss Chris Doyle and my work pal Cliona Hurson from 98FM – I will be forever grateful to you both for your support and slagging of course! Chris... thank you for 'turning a blind eye' to me blogging while in work... I know you knew the work was always done :)! Without 98FM, where my SoSueMe.ie journey began – I wouldn't be where I am today – so thank you!

To all my family and friends – you have all supported me in many different ways, but most of all, thank you for believing in me.

Lastly but by no means least – thank you, the readers! You all encourage and inspire me to keep doing what I'm doing! Thank you for being on this journey with me, some of you have been with me from the start and I hope you continue to grow with me and my blog as the years go on! I appreciate and love you all! And remember, dreams do come true if you work hard! :)

xxx

Dedication

I dedicate this book to my Mum and Dad!

You have both taught me everything I know! Thank you for the wonderful upbringing you gave me, I will be forever grateful! I don't think there is anything more important you can ask for in life than a happy and memorable childhood filled with love! I have that and thank you both! You are truly amazing parents and I love you both so very much.

Suzanne xx

CHAPTER ONE

So Who Am I?

A selection of pictures of me growing up. As you can see – my brother Rob and I were inseparable!

Summer 2003. I had failed a course I didn't even like, I had no idea where my life was going and I didn't have even the vaguest notion about what kind of career I wanted to build for myself! While all my friends were settling into college, I, on the other hand, had hit the proverbial wall, and for a time, it really seemed like not even a wrecking ball would be able to break through it.

Fast forward ten years, however, and my life had reached the other extreme. To be honest, I still struggle to take it all in sometimes. Earlier this year Diet Coke flew me to London as the official blogger to attend a red carpet, exclusive, invite-only press event hosted by none other than Marc Jacobs himself! Writers from the world's most influential fashion magazines and big time celebs filled the red carpet, and I found myself drifting into a moment pure bliss in my mind, thinking of what was going on around me, until the flashing of the paparazzi camera lights and the calling of my name snapped me back into reality.

That was the moment when it really hit me. I was one of them!

All of my hard work and dedication had led to me earning my place among these industry heavyweights! Well, I've always said determination will get you places, and, when I look back on my early childhood, the signs were certainly there that I was going to be one hell of a determined character.

When I arrived into the world in October 1984, strong independent figures dominated showbiz and media. They were everywhere! Prince was top of Billboard's Hot 100 Singles, Tina Turner was on the front cover of *Rolling Stone* magazine, and the insanely glamorous style icon, Joan Collins, was constantly on television. Frankly, I'm thrilled that I was a baby of the 80s! It was such a glam, glitter-filled, party era and I'm pretty sure it rubbed off on me!

80s icon Michael Jackson

Meeting Marc Jacobs and my piece for Star Chic magazine

Determined From Day One!

According to my parents, I was one year old when my determined nature made itself known.

I was always a Daddy's girl!

When I was born, the nurse turned to my mam, and asked if she had noticed that my toes were slightly turned under. The doctors later explained to my parents that they would have to wait until I had started walking before I could be brought back to hospital to have a procedure carried out in which the bones in my feet would be broken so that my toes could be reset. One year on, and of a Monday morning in Dublin's Holles Street Hospital, I was put to sleep ahead of the surgery. To this day, my mam always teases my dad about that morning, because he was sobbing his heart out like a baby after I was sedated for surgery! I was a real daddy's girl, and, truth be told, I still am!

I was discharged from hospital a few hours after surgery, however, the one thing that had my mam worried sick was how she was going to keep me off my feet. One of the instructions from the doctors was not to, under any circumstances, put ANY weight on the feet until they healed. That evening, while my mam was preparing the dinner, she had me strapped into the buggy so I couldn't go anywhere. A few minutes later the telephone rang, and as we didn't have a cordless phone back then, she had to go out into the hall to answer it. When the phone call ended, she turned around, and, to her amazement, I too was in the hallway, laughing as I walked on my fully-bandaged feet! All my mam and dad could do was laugh and cry with relief, because they could both see at that point that absolutely nothing was ever going to hold me back in life. I was a determined little divil, and that trait definitely stayed with me as I got older. According to Mam, I was always very independent and liked to do things for myself. When I was four years of age and starting school, I firmly insisted on taking the school bus alone, and paying Frank the driver myself.

Me and my dad today!

Loved my red shoes!

I later joined Irish dancing and ballet classes, which I thoroughly enjoyed, and have very fond memories of. I preferred Irish dancing though, and I really showed a talent for it, winning titles all over Ireland. That said, I was always getting into trouble. I was the one dancer who was forever interrupting the class! Either I would be chatting to the other girls about school, or else getting distracted by wanting to know what everyone was wearing.

Admittedly, I was extremely competitive, though in a nice way. I was confident in myself, and familiarised myself with the top dancers in my age category. I consistently trained hard, and was always super-prepared when competition time rolled around. I made sure I stayed on top by wearing the best costumes. I loved fashion even from a very early age, and, secretly, I think I preferred Irish dancing because of the element of pageantry that went with it! I got to have big curly hair, beautiful dresses and a little bit of makeup for the Feiseanna every Sunday! To this day, I remember my first Irish dancing costume so vividly. It was deep purple velvet with heavy beading, and it fitted like a glove. I had that costume for ages and I always felt like it brought out my inner dancing diva. It's always important to have a piece of clothing that just helps bring out your inner goddess and makes you feel amazing – that is what fashion has always been for me. When the item is right, you feel amazing!

I chose this outfit myself!

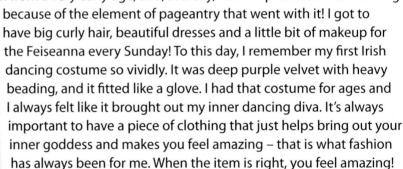

Education

Confirmation with friends Elaine and Niamh

Throughout my school years – primary and secondary – I was NEVER a grade A student. Never! I was always in the mediocre classes and never really knew what I wanted to do. At no point was I one of those girls who knew exactly what college she wanted to go to or what course she wanted to do. To be honest, I barely understood the CAO form! Something inside, however, always reassured me that I would be okay. I would eventually find my niche and I would make it work.

Once I left secondary school, that bright spark of career inspiration still hadn't hit. I am always asked if blogging was something I had wanted to do from the get-go, but, the truth is, for a long time, I had no clue what I wanted to do. I didn't even know what courses to go for. I looked over the ones that were available to me, one of which was a PLC course in Social Care. Admittance was based more on the interview than Leaving Cert points, so I went for it and was successful. I knew on the first day of the course that I was going to hate it, but I stuck it out for the year because I didn't want to be the only one of my friends not attending college. I was also the eldest in my family, and I didn't want my parents thinking that their first born was a failure. I gave the course a shot, but my heart wasn't in it. One class I did love was psychology. I learned so much about behaviour, and, in the long term, it paid off because it helped me to read people quite well.

Secondary school, 2000

The course in Social Care however, just wasn't to be. I remember my parents were away on holiday when I got a phone call from the head teacher asking me to come in for a meeting. The reason for the meeting could be summed up in his first line. "Look Suzanne, you failed the course." Admittedly, I was surprised, because even though I knew I wasn't going to get honours, I didn't think I was actually going to fail the bloody thing! I was so upset at the time, because, if I wanted to progress to the second stage, I would have to re-sit the entire first year. I didn't want to tell my parents that I had failed the course, so instead I told them that I passed the course but that I didn't want to continue with it as I felt it wasn't for me. (Yes, mam and dad, I lied!) They had always encouraged us to try everything, but to do what we enjoyed, so I knew they wouldn't mind me packing it in if I felt it wasn't right for me.

After I left college, I spent a few weeks lying in bed. In fact, it was my mum who pushed me to get a job or to at least do something that would get me up and out of bed! I secured a job in Topshop and loved every second of the year I spent working there. I loved the exposure I had to all the trends, learning the fashion terminology, and, I more than developed a love affair with the 85% staff discount! However, I didn't see much opportunity to

My debs with my first boyfriend, Conor McGonagle. We were together for 9 years.

progress within the business, so climbing the ladder wasn't going to happen as fast as I had wanted. Still, I loved helping girls piece together new looks, and so, I set my sights on becoming a Topshop style advisor. A style advisor was solely employed to style the customers who had booked them. Unfortunately, however, there were at least three or so girls ahead of me on the waiting list for such vacancies, so I knew it wasn't going to happen any time soon.

One day, I noticed a girl arrive into Topshop dressed head-to-toe in a beautiful white fitted dress with her hair sitting immaculately in a bun – she kind of reminded me of a nurse from that movie *Pearl Harbour*. She was glamorous and greeted me what a beaming smile. I was actually on duty in the changing rooms that day, so I struck up a conversation with her, I was dying to know what she did for a living. To my surprise, she explained she was studying beauty therapy in a college called Coogan Bergin in Dublin 2. She then went on to tell me about the course and how much she loved it. The whole thing sounded amazing, and, as she was talking about it, I remember thinking about how much I would love to do something similar. To be honest, I don't know why I didn't give a career in beauty therapy serious consideration much earlier. It was ideal for me! Even when I was in school, I was always the girl my classmates turned to if they ever needed a slick of lip gloss or mascara.

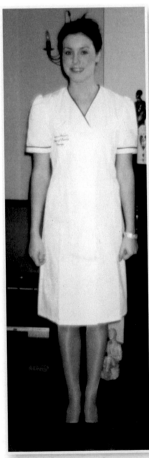

My first day at Coogan Bergin College of Beauty Therapy

After I told my parents about the conversation I'd had with the customer, we discussed my options, and looked at all the different beauty therapy courses available. In the end, the reviews about Coogan Bergin impressed us most, so I opted to go there. My parents paid the fee, which wasn't small by any means, but I think that's what really motivated me to apply myself and excel as much as I could. I work well under pressure, and, knowing that they had paid so much money for me to do the course really gave me that extra driving force I needed to succeed. The course was tough, and very science-based, but I loved it so much. During my year in Coogan Bergin, I learned all about anatomy, and physiology of the body, and I enthusiastically absorbed every ounce of information I could. It paid off, and, when exam time rolled around, I received all honours. I was pretty chuffed to find out that I was the only student in the college who had received honours in electrolysis as well. It was such a difficult subject, and, when I was starting out in it, I was so nervous, because it involved inserting a needle into the hair follicle to cut off the blood supply. Achieving honours in electrolysis really boosted my confidence because I had proved to myself that I was not a failure.

When I look back on how different things came about for me, I realise just how lucky a person I am. A lot of things that have swayed the course of my life for the better seem to have happened by chance. For instance, while I was in college with Coogan Bergin in 2006, I was working part-time in a shop called Echo. One day, the manager of Echo introduced me to a customer called Teresa, who happened to be the owner of The Haven Beauty Therapy Clinic in Balbriggan, which was the busiest beauty clinic in North County Dublin at the time. When my manager told Teresa that I was studying beauty therapy, she told me I could go to her if ever I needed work experience. I'm a very ballsy person, so I told her that I was qualifying that summer, and asked if she would consider me for a junior position within the salon. She agreed to see me once I had passed my exams.

If I want to do something, and I really put my mind to it, I can guarantee I will do it well, so, once I had set my sights on working in The Haven, I knew I would get there at some point. Sure enough, the moment I passed my exams, I knocked on Teresa's door. She stayed true to her word and started me in the salon on a trial basis, which subsequently led to a permanent position. I ended up working there for three years! Even though I was a junior, I had become the busiest therapist within the space of a year. Thanks to my intensive training in Coogan Bergin, I was good at what I did, and, as a result, I always ended up with the most bookings.

The role of a beautician is multi-layered. Your main role is to carry out procedures, but you are also a sales person. You are selling treatments, products, and, if you don't hit your weekly sales target, then you don't make a commission on top of your basic weekly wage. If you weren't nice to a customer, you wouldn't get a tip either. I was lucky in that clients liked my personality. I always remembered the little things they would say, whether it was about a wedding they had coming up, or a holiday they were going on, and whenever I would see them again, I would ask about it. They appreciated that personal touch. I was also quite good at reading a person's skin, and determining which products would suit them best. I never bluffed, I was always honest and upfront with them, and I think this is why I got so many repeat clients. They always found my recommendations produced results, and so, they trusted me. I think this is also why product recommendations have become a hugely popular feature on SoSueMe.

People assume beauty therapy is all about makeup, but that couldn't be further from the truth. Makeup artistry is a totally different career field. That's why I took a course

9

in the subject in Dun Laoghaire College. I studied makeup on Mondays and Tuesdays and then worked as a beautician on Wednesdays, Thursdays, Fridays and Saturdays. I was always busy, and always challenging myself, exposing myself to new areas that could be of benefit to me. Once I had the makeup qualification under my belt, I began to incorporate it into my duties in The Haven. I was run off my feet with work, but, I loved the makeup side of the job so I was delighted to be busy. I was also the only specialised waxing therapist in the salon at the time, so I was constantly being booked for appointments. All in all, life was good. Hectic, but good!

While The Haven was undoubtedly one of the best places I worked, there came a point where I wanted to move on. During my time there, I had become the top seller, the most booked-out beautician, and I had basically achieved all I could. I needed a new challenge.

With my sisters Carla and Katie and brother Robert

The only way to make good money as a beautician is to open up your own salon, but, during the boom times in Ireland, there were salons on every corner, and I most certainly couldn't have competed with established places such as The Haven, so it seemed pointless to even entertain the idea of opening up my own place.

When I decided I wanted to move on from beauty therapy, I hit that brick wall again. I had no idea what my next step would be, but I wasn't going to stay in a job where I wasn't happy. If I'm not happy with something, I don't dwell on it, I instead set about changing it. I began looking through different job vacancies online, and tried to figure out which area I would like to get into. That's how I came across the recruitment sector. When I read the job spec for recruitment consultant, it seemed very sales-orientated, and so, I knew I had the personality and the skill set to do it very well. At face value, it sounds mad that a beauty therapist from a salon in Balbriggan would apply for a job where she would be competing against people with degrees, but I figured there was no harm in taking the risk. I knew I had the ability, all I had to do was convince my interviewer!

I sent my CV to a big recruitment firm, and was called in for an interview. It didn't go as well as I had hoped, though admittedly, the outfit I chose to wear didn't help matters. In fact, I cringe when I think about how I dressed for that particular interview. Looking back, I still can't decide which part of the attire was worse – the fishnets, or, the red leather gloves! In my defence, I honestly thought that was the regular style for an office job.

I sat before my interviewer with everything prepared, but he had already decided he didn't like me. This was obvious from his belittling comments, and snide remarks. He was just a horrible guy; the kind who treated people as though they were beneath him. His attitude wasn't enough to deter me though. In fact, it motivated me even more. When

I went home, I applied for more recruitment positions. I was determined to get a job in that sector. As horrible as the previous interview had been, there was a silver lining to be found – I now knew exactly what questions to expect.

Next, I was called for an interview with Top People Recruitment which was based on Dublin's Harcourt Street. When I walked into the top floor office, the first thing that struck me was the interior. It reminded me of the office in *The Devil Wears Prada*. The whole place just looked so amazing. I met with the manager, a lovely woman called Nicki, and we got on brilliantly. She was a tough interviewer, but she liked me.

Nadia Power ©

Dressing for the office

During the interview, I used every detail I had at my disposal. I had no degree, and back then, everyone had degrees, so I instead honed in on my proven abilities, such as my sales experience. The job of a recruitment consultant is also based on building relationships, so I outlined all the skills I had acquired from my previous careers, and explained how I could apply them to a recruitment role. In the end, Nicki took a chance on me and I got the job. I loved it from the moment I started it. They trained me well, and there were always incentives there to motivate employees' performances. Achievements were always acknowledged, and there was a great sense of appreciation for your hard work. You also develop a really thick skin in that industry, which certainly stood to me in my blogging years!

Recruitment consultants had to bring in their own accounts, so I would cold call big businesses and ask if I could meet them. Within a year, I had brought in big accounts such as AXA Insurance, and Hibernian. Thanks to the money I was bringing in, I became one of the most successful consultants within the firm. It was such a great period in my life. I was 22 years of age, driving a brand new Toyota Celica, living in a fabulous apartment with my best friend, and shopping non-stop. Of course, this was during the boom years when commission money was ridiculously high. I think back now and kick myself for not saving some of it! HR was the backbone of every company, and so, it paid big money, because, at the time, everyone was hiring.

Hooked on Instagram!

I remained with Top People for around three years, and although I loved it, I had learned all I could with them, so my frame of mind centred around finding the next challenge. It was at that stage that I applied for the job of

HR consultant with Hibernian. I remember thinking there was no way I would get the job, because they were looking for seriously experienced people with HR qualifications, which I didn't have, but then, I figured I had nothing to lose by throwing my name into the ring, so I applied for the Hibernian job, and was called for an interview. I underwent four interviews in total, as well as a behavioural test.

To my shock, I was offered the job! I was probably the least experienced of the candidates who applied, but, I genuinely think it comes down to having the balls to go for something. I knew I didn't have the most experience, but I convinced myself I did. That's the way I have always been. Even if I didn't really believe I could do something, I would convince myself I could, and then just go for it. I also prepared in every way possible. Preparation is key for success in whatever you aim for.

Push ba

With my bestie, Sara

I told my boss in Top People that I had been offered the job with Hibernian, and almost immediately, I was presented with an offer of an increased salary and commission stake, as well as a number of additional incentives. They were determined to keep me there, and, because I loved them, I stayed. The owner of Top People, Michael O'Leary, was such a gentleman and always treated his staff very well. You see, in the recruitment industry, you are only a number, and your worth is measured by your previous month's sales figure, so, when I saw how badly they wanted me to stay, it made me feel slightly more secure. Michael O'Leary himself, the MD, sent me an email that day explaining how happy he was that I decided to stay on in Top People and he wanted to sit down with me for coffee the following week to discuss my future plans within the company – I felt very proud and extremely content at that time! He was always such an inspiring man and to this day – I am thankful for my job at Top People recruitment, I learned so much!

Looking back, however, I do regret not taking the HR job. Even though Hibernian's HR department was made redundant a year later as a result of cutbacks, it is still a regret of mine that I didn't take the opportunity they had offered me. That said, I'm a firm believer in the theory that 'what's for you won't pass you', so, on the other hand, maybe it was meant to work out the way it did.

the best revenge is massive success.

Frank Sinatra

Shortly after I turned down the job with Hibernian, the recession hit, and I was made redundant from the recruitment industry. I had gone from enjoying a high powered position with an amazing salary and lots of perks, to suddenly being unemployed, and living on social welfare for a few months. It was a crushing knock back to square one. I hated that period of my life. I felt depressed, and I was back at that horrible point of uncertainty where I didn't know what my next step would be. The funny thing is, whenever I hit these 'walls' in life, I always knew things would turn good for me eventually. I don't know why, but I also had a gut feeling I would one day become 'known', isn't that weird!

When I was made redundant in March 2009, I didn't know what to do or where to turn. I had no income. A few of my friends were modelling at the time and my friend Joanne encouraged me to go into her agency, Bscene, for a chat with the owners, Seán and Brendan. That's what I did, and they liked my look and said I had a good height – 5'8'. They signed me straight away and I was delighted with myself. I knew it wasn't going to pay

One of my early modelling jobs

the bills long-term, but it was a start. From then on, I did lots of fun photo shoots, appeared on TV with TV3's Xposé and Ireland AM, and was in the papers some days for different product launches. That year, I also got to enter Miss Universe Ireland after winning a heat of 30 girls for the Miss Hotspot.ie title. I was so happy, and modelling even let to me becoming the face of O2 for a year. It was an amazing experience, but I still craved something that provided me with a secure income. When I was searching for jobs online, I came across a part-time receptionist position with Dublin's 98FM. I think that's when it really hit me that I had gone from a successful career to a part-time job. It was a very low time, but I still applied for the job because I just wanted to feel like I was back in employment again. I always see the positive side of every situation, and, in this case, I figured the silver lining was that the job would expose me to the media industry.

Radio

I underwent a tough interview with the CEOs of Spin and 98FM. Even though the job itself was kind of crap by comparison to what I had done previously, I so badly wanted to work in that office from the moment I walked through the doors. It was such a stylish, modern, environment. Everyone strolled around in casual wear, chatting and laughing. It seemed like such a fun place to work! Even the little screens that displayed the presenters on air in the reception area gave me a warm fuzzy feeling – I dug media and really wanted to work there after my interview. Fortunately, I was offered the job and I started working there in November 2009. I didn't know it, but this would be the job that would effectively change my life!

There were so many celebrities passing through the studio doors of 98FM. It wasn't unusual to see One Direction, Russell Brand, Diversity, or JLS wandering in on any given day. That's when it occurred to me that this was something I could write about from the perspective of a normal girl working on a reception desk. I always read international blogs, never Irish ones, because, at the time, there were no decent Irish ones that caught my attention. There was definitely a niche in the home market.

Sporting the 98FM Oxegen poncho

With 98FM music programmer Gavin Ward

The more I thought about it, the more the idea gathered momentum. Eventually, I bit the bullet and started putting a plan together. First I needed a name. I asked a friend for some suggestions, and together, we brainstormed all the usual names like 'Sue's Diary', etc, but still, nothing stood out. After going through a variety of titles, we hit on, 'Sue Me', and that's when the penny dropped! The blog should be called SoSueMe!

Myself and the insanely beautiful Ashley Banjo from Diversity

Meeting The Wanted

With The Script

CHAPTER TWO

SO SUE ME

FASHION • BEAUTY • SHOWBIZ

By Suzanne Jackson

FASHION ▾   BEAUTY ▾   SHOWBIZ ▾   WIN!!   SHOP SUE'S STYLE   SUE'S BLOG ▾   YOUTUBE   CONTACT US ▾

DON'T MISS

Rihanna's "Styled To Rock" New Season Gets Some Huge Stars!!

Khloe Kardashian Helps Kylie Jenner Dye Her Hair Blue!!

Jessica Alb

Search So Sue Me

SEARCH HERE!   **SEARCH**

REVIEW: Seoid Spa at Dunboyne Castle Hotel!

REVIEW: Bourjois Volume Glamour Max Mascara!

My BIG NEWS (Part 2): I Signed A Book Deal!!!!

My Top 5 Foundations – Pharmacy & High End!!

DIARY BLOG: My Day At London Fashion Week 2013!

Posted **September 21, 2013** by **Suzanne Jackson** in <u>Beauty</u>

💬 <u>4 Comments</u>

My Top 5 Foundations – Pharmacy & High End!!

Motel
25% OFF
SELECTED
LINES

So Sue Me

I didn't expect the blog to become as big as it did, but, at the same time, I wanted to ensure that should it ever become a huge hit, it would have to have the type of name that people would remember. I also wanted the name to be a potential brand name. SoSueMe seemed to fit the bill! In a way, I was always thinking ahead, and always thinking big!

The first SoSueMe blog!

Now that I had the name in place and the blog set up, I needed content.

Jedward were due into the studio one day, and, given that they had just left X-Factor, and Jedmania was at its height, their visit seemed like the perfect topic for my first post. I wrote about how normal they were. Yes, totally mad, but still normal! It got me a few readers, but nothing phenomenal.

The blog was only two days old when something remarkable happened. I had been photographed at a social event a week earlier, the pictures of which appeared on an Irish website called Showbiz.ie. Long before the term 'internet troll' was even coined, this site was famous for them! They would comment on photos and generally leave a stream of hateful comments, all anonymously, of course. Some of the remarks were genuinely horrible, sometimes even downright personal. When my photograph was posted on the site, someone left a bitchy comment asking, "who does Suzanne Jackson think she is, setting up a blog?" They then added, "only deluded people would read her shit blog". This was accompanied by a link to my SoSueMe blog. Almost immediately, people started jumping on the bandwagon and contributing their own nasty remarks. It reached a point where my friends started contacting me to see if I was aware of what was being said about me on the forum. The initial comment really stung, mainly because it was made by someone I knew. The only place I had posted a link to my new blog was on my personal Facebook page, so whoever had posted that comment on Showbiz.ie was obviously someone on my Facebook friends list! Typical.

When I read that comment, I genuinely considered not pursuing the blog idea any further. I was already involved in the modelling industry, so, in a way, I was somewhat prepared for bitchiness, though granted, I wasn't expecting such a strong degree of bitchiness so fast! After all, the blog was only a few days old. On the other hand, it drew attention to my blog, so I ended up with a large number of new fans who still read the blog to this day! In fact, maybe I should take this opportunity to thank the girl who posted that first bitchy comment! ;-)

On the encouragement of my friends, I decided I would keep going with SoSueMe. I am often asked if I had a set plan in mind for the blog. I honestly didn't. It just morphed into a blog consisting of showbiz, beauty and fashion. After all, I was surrounded by showbusiness thanks to both my job at the front desk of 98FM, and, my involvement in the modelling industry. With my background in beauty and my love of cosmetics, it was inevitable that they would be included in the blog as well. Fashion, likewise, seemed like an obvious topic to feature in the blog as I adored style and was familiar with the ins and outs of the industry thanks to my previous job in Topshop.

When the blog was only a couple of weeks old, the hits were high, around five hundred or so a day. A friend of mine, Raul, was heavily involved in IT, and it was he who persuaded me to think about turning the blog into a proper website. He also suggested that I buy the domain name, SoSueMe.ie, before someone else robbed it! Good thinking on his part, without a doubt. The tech business was completely foreign to me, but, with the help of Raul, we set up a pretty website for me to work from. It was very basic, but it was a great way to get started.

Some time later, I met a web designer called Simone, who was helping to re-brand the 98FM website. I always had a vision of exactly how I wanted the SoSueMe website to look, so I asked Simone if she could help me design a proper template and logo.

My beloved nanny!

I told her what I wanted, we exchanged ideas and then her quote came in. Simone quoted €1,200, not much to some but a lot when I was on part-time receptionist wages! That evening, I had a chat with mam and dad who were always so encouraging and dad arranged that my nanny (his mam) would lend me the money if I would commit to paying her back to €200 a month… which I did. It was a big risk and a lot of money to bank on something that might not work out. Many would have argued that there were a lot of similar blogs around at the time, but I was confident I could bring mine to a level of success that would outshine the rest. I had big plans, it was just a matter of putting them into action.

I was adamant that SoSueMe should be of a style similar to a magazine. At the time, the recession had hit, and people seemed to be turning to the web to get their showbiz fix, as opposed to spending money on actual magazines. I discussed my ideas with Simone, and, together, we planned the new SoSueMe website. I still remember how exciting it felt to get the whole thing up and running. Within three weeks, she had re-branded SoSueMe and redesigned the entire site. Simone really gave it that gloss that I was looking for. With the new design, the readership grew, and I was so happy that I'd invested money in SoSueMe.ie!

As the blog started to grow, so too did the number of fans on the SoSueMe Facebook page. I really concentrated my efforts on growing the Facebook page as much as I did the blog itself, because I knew that social media would help drive traffic to the blog. I also made the Facebook page very image-focused. I would upload an image relating to the story, accompanied by a link to the website where the story itself could be read in full.

The first SoSueMe.ie design, by Simone!

SoSueMe, today!

18

At the time, most blogs would upload just the links, which made their pages seem quite boring and text heavy. My use of images, however, really caught peoples' attention, and so, the traffic to the website increased.

I posted a blog post once a day on SoSueMe and although my 98FM boss Chris Doyle knew I was writing my blog during work hours, he turned a blind eye to it.
He knew the work was being done, so he didn't mind that I was also blogging as well.

He could have stopped me if he wanted to, but he didn't, and I think I'll be forever grateful to him for that!

Working and blogging!

...on a few occasions, they even allowed me on air!

Chris was probably the best boss I have ever had and when I was torn between the idea of leaving 98FM this year to pursue SoSueMe full time or staying where I was, he was so encouraging and he really gave me the fire in my belly to do it.

So Chris, if you're reading this, thank you for your continued support!

Working in a popular radio station not only furnished me with a wealth of PR contacts within the industry, it also allowed me direct access to the celebrities and well-known personalities that passed through its doors. If it wasn't for 98FM, I probably wouldn't even have a blog today.

SoSueMe's 1st Birthday

Within no time at all, SoSueMe was heading toward the big one year old! My little baby blog that had brought me so much happiness and fulfilment through the year was turning one! I toyed with the idea of throwing a 1st birthday party and after posting a status to my own personal Facebook page about whether or not to do it, my mind was made up! Everyone thought it was a great idea and they all wanted to come!

I was particularly good at networking and this really stood to me in the long run. If your blog is to be successful, you need to have strong contacts. Being on the front desk of 98FM, I was constantly speaking to people in the entertainment industry. I was always collecting email addresses for PR companies, so that I could send them a brief synopsis of the blog. Believe me, the products don't just automatically come flying in when you start a blog. You have to invest time and work into establishing your site and profile. I invested huge time and effort in contacting the relevant people, and, in the end, my networking paid off.

When I held SoSueMe's first birthday on July 15th 2011 in the Grafton Lounge, I didn't expect many people to turn up, but that said, I had greatly underestimated the growing popularity of the blog. I decided to make a big event of the night, and even supplied those in attendance with goodie bags from various sponsors. It all helped to create a buzz around my blog, and, overall, it was a fab way to mark a successful first year in business. I grabbed every opportunity I could to get publicity for SoSueMe, so a bonus to the night was that the event also enjoyed some coverage in the newspapers.

One of SoSueMe's talented readers, Marie Claire, made cupcakes for the party! How amazing!

A SoSueMe reader

With fellow models, Hayley Ryan and Michele McGrath

With my friends and readers

Myself and radio DJ Ray Shah

Two of my best friends, Joanne and Sara

Dublin designer Emma Manley

Me with my sister Carla

Hayley Ryan and Michele McGrath

With my mam and dad

Myself and my pal Joanne

21

After the birthday bash, SoSueMe continued to grow as quickly as before and I feel my second year blogging was when I really started to learn about what worked for me. I had tested the water with different types of blog posts, and I'd noticed the trends and found which posts readers really liked. In year one the site was heavy on fashion and showbiz articles, but in year two I really found my niche. I noticed that my personal blog posts had the highest readership figures so I honed in on that and wrote from my point of view. I put the Sue twist on things and found that my What I Wore blog posts went down a treat, especially since 90% of my wardrobe is from the high street which readers loved!

I also had a big hit with the Beauty Product Review section. I find it amazing that brands almost always sell out of products and outfits that I recommend. I suppose this is because I am 100% honest in my reviews and would never feature something that I don't like.

After I found my niche within the blogging world, SoSueMe grew and grew and as the summer of 2012 drew to a close, I had an interesting phone call. Andrea Roche of Andrea Roche Modelling Agency invited me to enter a Miss SoSueMe girl into the Miss Universe Ireland beauty pageant, which she manages in association with Donald Trump's Miss Universe. Andrea felt that from a brand perspective I was now big enough to enter a girl and thought that it would be a great move for SoSueMe – she was right!

Straight away I thought it was a fantastic idea. My readers are mostly female, aged between 16-35, and a large percentage of them ask about modelling and how to get into it. What better opportunity for me to help a reader enter the world of modelling? I got working straight away!

Photo © Patrick O'Leary

With the first ever Miss SoSueMe Mairead O'Farrell!

Miss SoSueMe 2012

When I was in the midst of organising Miss SoSueMe 2012, I remember posting a Facebook status that said, "Hats off to any career event organisers out there!" I meant every word of it!

It was without a doubt the most challenging event I have ever organised, even by comparison to the memorably-stressful organising of SoSueMe's 1st birthday! It was all worth it though, and the first ever Miss SoSueMe Pageant turned out to be a huge success!

Hosted by 98FM's Siobhan O'Connor and Steven Cooper in the surroundings of Dublin's award winning Wright Venue, 32 gorgeous girls competed for the title of Miss SoSueMe,

the winner of which would then go forward to compete for the title of Miss Universe Ireland.

Each judge knew the beauty and pageant world inside out, so I completely trusted them to find the right girl to represent the SoSueMe brand. The judging panel consisted of top model and former Miss Universe Ireland Roz Purcell, former Miss Ireland Holly Carpenter, TV presenter and model, Daniella Moyles, former *Britain & Ireland's Next Top Model* contestant, Hannah Devane, model and former *Big Brother* contestant Orlaith McAllister, top fashion photographer, Evan Doherty, TV personality and model, Emily MacKeogh, fashion guru to the celebs Lara Casey, and top male models, Brook Wright and Gerard Smith.

The crown was eventually awarded to the stunning and very deserving winner, Mairead O'Farrell from Cork! Mairead was a beautiful person inside and out, and definitely worthy of the Miss SoSueMe sash.

Miss SoSueMe winner Mairead O'Farrell and the 1st and 2nd runners up

23

Sam, Dave and Michelle

Of course no blog tell all story is ever complete without the recognition of my fellow writers – my SoSueMe Dream Team! Without these three guys, SoSueMe wouldn't be as big as it is today! Bringing extra voices to a blog is always a positive. It can get boring listening to the one person harping on – so I like to mix things up a little with a blog post a week from my fellow writers, Dave, Sam and Michelle.

I always knew Sam, a girl who lived near me, lived, ate and breathed fashion. Sam, who was working as a manager for Vera Moda had her own distinctive style, which I knew would appeal to a large audience bracket. Sam has great taste in fashion, and when I wrote a blog post about recruiting an additional SoSueMe writer in 2011, Sam applied straight away! When I saw her CV land in my inbox, I knew I wanted her! I called her that evening and Sam started straight away Sam has now been writing for me for two years and even has her own fan following – which is always great to see. Sam has not only become a trusted and fellow writer but a best friend. We both have such a passion for SoSueMe and so when something gets us down or we're having an off day, 9 times out of 10 we will always ring each other. Sam's friendly, kind natured attitude and persona is so uplifting and she always knows how to cheers me up, and visa versa.

With current SoSueMe writer Samantha Gibbons and former contributor Derek O'Sullivan

Following the release of Rhianna's new film *Battleship* in 2012, I secured movie première tickets as a prize for a competition I wanted to run. A guy called Dave Higgins won, and, the day after the film, he very sweetly mailed me a review of it. Immediately I spotted a great opportunity. I was constantly being invited to every film première in town, but I didn't want to review the films, because that had never been my area. I phoned Dave and asked him if he wanted to be a film reviewer for SoSueMe. It was an unpaid internship, but the benefit was that he would get to attend every new film. His pieces were popular, and so, he became SoSueMe's trusted movie reviewer.

I have since taken on a new girl called Michelle Strutt who writes about show business and fashion. I always trust my instinct, and so I know Michelle, like Sam and Dave, will be a huge asset to SoSueMe. They are my dream team and I know that without them, SoSueMe wouldn't be as big as it is today.

SUZANNE
So Sue Me

How fab is my personalised illustration by Holly Shorthall? I love it!

THAT wedding dress picture!

By October 2012, I had 18,000 fans on my page. It took me two years of solid hard work to get to that point, so now you see what I mean when I say that there is no quick route to success! A year later, however, in October 2013, the popularity of the Facebook page had spiralled and SoSueMe had over 85,000 fans! The readership of the blog was also on the rise.

I was always consistent in producing material for the blog, and this definitely helped increase my range, however what really catapulted the blog into the big figures, was a random picture of a wedding dress that I posted. I had found the photo on the scrapbook site, Pinterest, and, believe it or not, I actually debated putting it up on the SoSueMe Facebook page. The dress in question was quite lace-heavy, and given that not a lot of people like lace, I figured the response would be pretty divided. Or so I thought! I uploaded the picture and accompanied it with the caption, "Yay or nay? I love it!"

In the space of 24 hours, the number of 'likes' on the photo had spiralled from 500, to 50,000! It had officially gone viral. Hundreds of thousands of people went on to share the photo, and, within the space of a few weeks, over one million people had liked it!

The readership numbers continued to rocket after I uploaded that picture, but, it helped that the brand name was distinctive. SoSueMe was unusual and people were interested to find out more about it when they saw it in their newsfeed. The designer of the dress herself emailed me to say she couldn't believe the huge interest in the dress that week and gave me all the details on how my readers could purchase it! You just never know who is reading your blog or checking out your Facebook page – here was a designer all the way from Brazil emailing me in relation to the reaction from my Facebook photo? Mental! I think this whole story will go down in history as a serious fluke!

I later discovered that the picture had ranked as one of the most 'viral' Facebook photos of the year! My 12-year-old sister, Katie, was googling SoSueMe one day, when an article from the website, Business Insider, appeared in the search listings.

The wedding dress that went viral!

25

In it, SoSueMe's wedding dress photo, was listed at number five on the list of the most 'viral' Facebook photos of 2012.

I firmly believe that if you work hard, karma will reward you well, and luck will strike when you need it. That wedding dress photograph was definitely my stroke of luck. People sometimes think my life is one long beach party. Trust me, it's not! I have had my own crosses to bear, and my own personal issues to deal with, but, in terms of business and success, I have worked extremely hard for everything that has come my way.

I am always being asked about my early life, and how SoSueMe came to be what it is today, so I really hope this chapter has answered your questions. I still can't quite believe how much SoSueMe has sky-rocketed since that first post back in 2009! On an average night out, I am stopped at least twenty times by different girls, and asked if I will stand for a picture. My boyfriend, Dylan, is also recognised from the blog, and he too often gets asked to stand in for a photograph.

It's crazy to think how I once considered shelving the idea of SoSueMe! If you take any message from this book, it is to follow whatever goals you set for yourself, never give up, and, if ever people belittle your plans or attempt to discourage you in any way, just remember the words of Frank Sinatra, "The best revenge is massive success!"

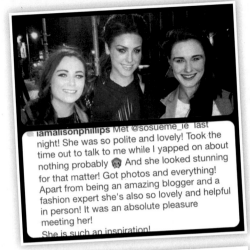

Iamalisonphillips Met @sosueme_ie last night! She was so polite and lovely! Took the time out to talk to me while I yapped on about nothing probably 😜 And she looked stunning for that matter! Got photos and everything! Apart from being an amazing blogger and a fashion expert she's also so lovely and helpful in person! It was an absolute pleasure meeting her! She is such an inspiration!

Jennifer Collins
@xJennyCxx

@SoSueMe_ie had my German exam today and we were asked bout blogs and wrote bout yours :-) #1moreleft #ThankYou

sarah walsh
@Sara___Walsh

@SoSueMe_ie My Obsession with you reached new levels today when i even mentioned you in a German exam #InLove #FeelFreeToBlockMe

Just a few of SoSueMe's sweetest fans!

Take chances.

All Experiences Count!

You have just seen from my own personal story how the different experiences in my life all contributed, in some way, to the success of SoSueMe. When I was working in HR, I learned about business and how to build relationships with companies. My job in Topshop taught me the ins-and-outs of the fashion industry; while my career in beauty therapy taught me all about skincare. My training as a makeup artist provided me with everything I needed to know about cosmetics and product application. Even my receptionist job was beneficial, as it exposed me to the media and showbiz industries, not to mention the celebrity figures who occupied them!

"In order to move on, you must understand why you felt what you did and why you no longer need to feel it."

— Mitch Albom, *Five People You Meet in Heaven*

WHEN SOMETHING BAD HAPPENS YOU HAVE THREE CHOICES. YOU CAN EITHER LET IT DEFINE YOU, LET IT DESTROY YOU, OR YOU CAN LET IT STRENGTHEN YOU.

factsaboutyou

FAITH is like Wi-Fi, it's invisible but it has the power to connect you to what you need.

QUOTEDIARY.ME

THE HAPPIEST PEOPLE DON'T HAVE THE BEST OF EVERYTHING, THEY JUST MAKE THE BEST OF EVERYTHING.

Be DRIVEN with purpose. Be RELENTLESS in your alignment with EXCELLENCE. Pay no mind to the disimpassioned impotent HATERS.

-Dr. Steve Maraboli

SUCCESSFUL PEOPLE NEVER WORRY ABOUT WHAT OTHERS ARE DOING.

KUSHANDWIZDOM

Don't wait for someone to bring you flowers. Plant your own garden and decorate your own soul.

First you had SoSueMe the blog… now you have SoSueMe the book! And under no circumstances are you to leave it on your living room shelf. I want you to keep it on your dressing table for whenever you need makeup tips, leave it on your desk for those days you need blogging advice, or perhaps carry it in your handbag for when you need some on-the-go style inspiration.

I am asked dozens of questions every day by the lovely readers of SoSueMe. How did I start blogging, what did I study in college, how did I set up my blog, what is my skincare routine, where do I like to shop, what clothing pieces should every girl own… and so I figured what better way to answer all these questions than to write a book?

I also wanted to share with you my own personal experience of how I created such a successful blog. My story is proof that hard work, determination, and consistency are so crucial to success. Brains and qualifications will only get you so far. Trust me, it's the other factors that really matter.

Throughout these chapters, you will see my 'Blogger Tips' which highlight why different techniques and topics are popular with readers and should help you to get in the blogging mindset while also hopefully learning some new beauty tricks! Once you've learned about how to write for an audience, the blogging chapter at the end will teach you everything you need to know about setting up a blog for the first time.

I am no expert in any of the fields I have discussed in this book, I am simply sharing with you everything I have learned about blogging, beauty, and fashion. Each section carries with it an array of topics and tutorials I know you will love!

I want this book to be your ultimate glamour guide, so go ahead and fold down the page corners, thumb through the chapters, and place bookmarks in the sections you want to return to. Put it to good use! I want you to thoroughly enjoy every single page of this book, and I really hope you have as much fun reading it as I did writing it.

Always remember to believe in yourself. Work hard and be nice.

> IN DOING SOMETHING, DO IT WITH LOVE OR NEVER DO IT AT ALL
>
> GANDHI

> i can't tell you the key to success, but the key to failure is trying to please everyone.
>
> *ed sheeran*

The best things in life:
Accidentally overhearing someone say something nice about you.
Waking up and realizing you still have a few hours left to sleep.
First kisses.
Making new friends and spending time with the old ones.
Singing in the bathroom.
Sweet dreams.
Hot chocolate.
Making brownies and cookies.
Holding hands with someone you care about.
Watching a sunset.
Sleeping in.
Taking long, hot showers
Starbucks.
Knowing that somebody misses you.

To the ones who still believe in dreams:

Chase them. Chase them until you're out of breath. Then, keep running.

there are so many people out there who will tell you that you can't. what you've got to do is turn around and say "watch me." -unknown

"BE STRONG, YOU NEVER KNOW WHO YOU ARE INSPIRING"

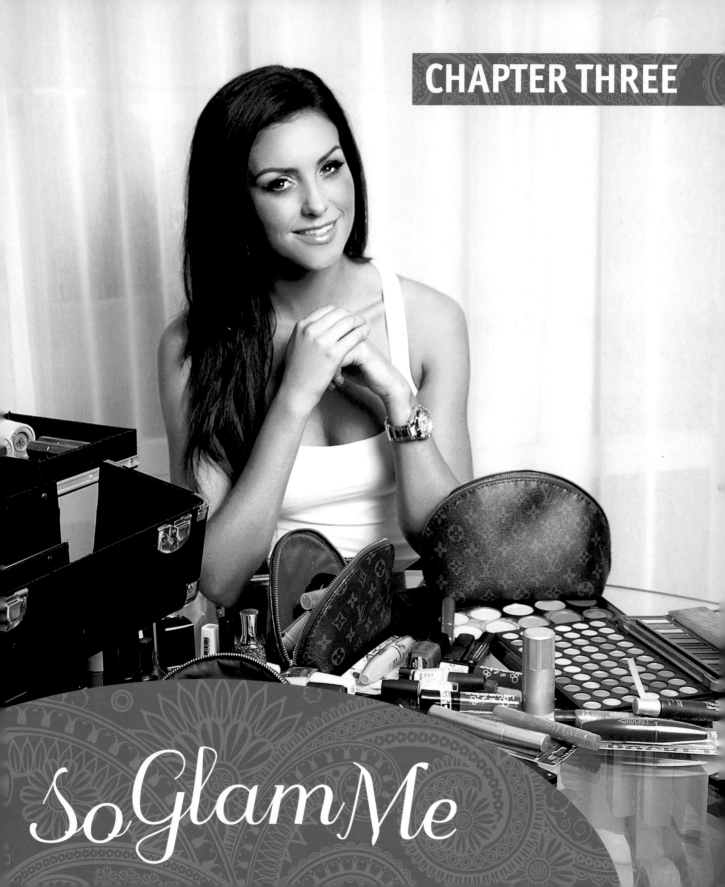

CHAPTER THREE

SoGlamMe

The first person I really thought of as beautiful was my mother. My mam was, and still is, one of the most beautiful women I know. Beautiful from the inside out. I remember many nights sitting at the end of her bed watching her get ready, whether it was for a night out with the girls, or a date night with my dad, my mam had a beauty regime and I used to get lost watching her.

She would sit at her vanity table, roll her silky blonde hair, and apply red lipstick to her beautiful full Angelina Jolie lips! I always wanted to have big lips like my mam, and she remembers me at a very young age saying, "Mam, I wish I had your lips, so I could apply loads of lipstick too!"

I was beauty obsessed, and it followed me right through to my later years. Makeup in the 80s wasn't how it is now. Back then, it was powdery and highly scented, and all you wanted to do was eat it. I absolutely loved it! Some nights, my mam would hand me a near empty lipstick to play with, and I too would sit with her applying my lipstick as if I was 21.

Finding my 'look' through my teens and 20s was a bumpy road and there were a lot of lessons learned along the way! We all over-plucked our brows at one point, we lightened our hair too much, we wore the total WRONG shade of foundation, and we definitely overdid it on the blusher and bronzer. Disaster yes, but then no lesson learned is ever a waste.

Fortunately for me, when I accidentally fell into the entertainment industry, it had its beauty perks, such as access to the best hair and makeup artists out there, whether it be at events, meetings, or shoots. To this day, if I am having my makeup done by a makeup artist, I will still ask a million questions. You can never know enough, and it's always good to get another person's opinion!

I see this beauty chapter as an opportunity for me to share everything I have learned from years of visiting many a makeup chair and hair salon.

Remember, sometimes less really is more. Beauty is not about hiding behind a layer of cosmetics, it's about becoming the best possible version of you, and feeling like you look the very best you can.

I hope you enjoy!

Sue xx

Highlighting And Contouring

Have you ever looked at your favourite celebrities and wondered how their skin and bone structure always look picture perfect, especially in comparison to how they look when photographed without makeup? Stars such as Kim Kardashian and J-Lo always seem to have the most beautifully chiselled cheekbones, defined noses, and seemingly flawless complexions. Well the secret is nothing more than good contouring. If there is one thing I am constantly asked about in the lovely emails you guys send me, it has got to be, "how do I contour?"

The power of highlighting and shading is a skill all on its own. In fact, when you contour correctly, you can give your face a completely different look. Using the right contouring makeup tricks, you can create the illusion of a slender nose, sleeker jaw line, all-over slimmer face and even more defined boobs! I have discussed contouring on my blog in the past, especially after Kim Kardashian posted pictures of her contour routine to her Twitter page back in 2012. Her 'selfies' prompted a huge surge in the number of ladies wanting to know how it was done.

When you contour correctly, you can give your face a completely different look.

Contouring forms an important part of my makeup routine whenever I am getting ready to go out at the weekend. I used to use a range of bronzers and highlighters to achieve the contoured look, but lately, I have switched to using cream-based concealers instead. I particularly love the results I get from my Crown Brush Concealer Palette, and it's super affordable too. I find that the cream-based concealers give a longer lasting, more natural looking contour. If you want to start using cream to contour, just make sure to apply it after your foundation and before your setting powder.

Before we get into the 'how to' section, remember, not everyone needs to contour. If you feel that your cheekbones are prominent enough (lucky you!), or, that your face has a nice thin shape already (lucky you again!), then it's best not to contour, as you may appear too 'chiselled' looking. Another thing to remember is, contouring takes practice, so don't give up!

With my Crown Contour Palette!

How to...Contour

Here is what you will need:

* Foundation matching your natural skin tone.
* Cream foundation, or, concealer x2 shades lighter than your natural skin tone.
* Cream foundation, or, concealer x2 shades darker colour than your natural skin tone.
* A foundation brush that is flat and a little pointed at the tip. (I like Crown C201 Oval Foundation Brush.)
* Blending brush, such as, Crown C406 Large Duo Fibre Foundation brush.
* Powder brush. (My favourite is Crown SS022 Jumbo Powder.)
* Setting powder. (I particularly like The Smashbox Translucent Powder.)

Crown C406 Large Duo Fibre Foundation brush

Sue's Step-by-Step...Contour Guide

Contour (darker colour)

Step 1 First apply the foundation that matches your skin tone.

Step 2 Starting with the darker colour, apply it under your cheekbone area – extending from the centre of your ear in a slightly downward motion to the lip area.

Step 3 Moving onto the side of the face, apply the darker colour into the temples and along the hairline on the top of the forehead.

Step 4 Using a small eye-shadow brush, softly line both sides of the nose. If your nose is long, you may want to apply a little under the tip of your nose. Again, keep the applications concise.

Step 5 Apply your darker colour below your jawbone, making sure not to apply any colour to the actual bone. The point is to create a shadow below your jaw. If your jaw is large, you may bring the contour colour up on either side of the chin. This will make your jaw appear less pronounced.

Step 6 Do NOT blend yet.

Highlight (lighter colour)

Step 1 Taking a small flat foundation brush, apply the lighter colour to your under eye area bringing it up to meet the darker colour in the temples.

Step 2 Apply it in the middle of your forehead and down the centre of your nose.

Step 3 Next, apply the lighter colour on the brow bone just underneath the arch of your eyebrows.

Step 4 Now sweep the colour along your jaw line, and not forgetting the collar bone itself.

Step 5 Highlight the centre of your chin, and I also recommend highlighting your cupid's bow (I.e. the arch on your top lip) for a more full, defined mouth.

Don't forget to check out my YouTube video on contouring!

Right now, you will most likely look like a clown, but that's okay! It means you did it right.

So now, it's time to blend. Using your foundation brush, start blending everything in a circular motion. Although your colours may be dramatic, there should be no severe lines when you are finished, so make sure you blend the edges well. You will be surprised by how easy this is, and how great it looks instantly!

Next up, powder! You need to set in place all your hard work, so it's important that you use a large powder brush to do this, and not a puff, otherwise you will smudge the look. I really love the Crown powder brush because it's soft and it applies the powder nicely!

To finish off this look, I always apply a little shimmer or bronzer on my cheekbones followed by a touch of blush on the apples of my cheeks. This will give you that fresh, even, sun-kissed skin tone, just like the celebs!

The Celebrity Choice – Mascara

For long, thick lashes, actress Kate Beckinsale relies on the worldwide phenomenon, Maybelline Great Lash Mascara. When asked about her beauty buys, Kate once told an interviewer, "a lot of fancy mascaras flake and get cakey, but Maybelline's Great Lash Mascara is really cheap and you can get it anywhere".

Davina McCall, Alexa Chung, Britney Spears and Rachel Bilson are also said to be huge fans of the cult product. WAG, Alex Gerrard, meanwhile, prefers Maybelline's Colossal Mascara, and, once wrote in her magazine beauty column, "I've bought about five different mascaras recently. My best one is the Maybelline Colossal Mascara. It gives you tons of volume, but it doesn't feel like you have lots on".

False Lashes

I have always been a lash queen! I absolutely looove long, glamorous, lashes that just open up your eyes, and I blame the Disney characters for this! When I was a kid, I would just look at Jasmine and Pocahontas with such envy. I loved them and I really wanted to be them. They always had the most amazing eyes and fluttery lashes, which, of course, fuelled my love for fake lashes later on in life.

From the first day I began wearing lashes, I could NEVER find the 'perfect' ones for me. I wanted lashes like Jasmine. I used to always say to my mam, that one day I would love to design my own range, and well, that wish finally came true!

I have created and designed an amazing lash line of seven stunning styles, which are available online now from sosuemelashes.com and in Harvey Nichols (€12.95). It literally took me five meetings to approve my lash range. I wanted them to be absolutely perfect, and we got there in the end!

Wearing my new range of fake lashes which are available from sosuemelashes.com!

My lashes are 100% real human hair. I prefer human hair eye lashes for a few different reasons. Real human hair false lashes are made to blend in better with your lashes, and give a more natural appearance. They have more give in them than synthetic lashes, and they can be bent to the shape of your eye so that they are worn ultra-comfortably. The seven styles will suit everyone. There is definitely a pair in there to suit you all! Some are dramatic and flirty, while others are pared back and natural looking. Whatever your look may be, SoSueMe Lashes will fast become your lash fix!

The 7 styles are:

* ★ Diamond Cluster
* ★ Champagne Kisses
* ★ Red Carpet Glam
* ★ Paparazzi Dream
* ★ VIP Luxury
* ★ Spotlight Attention
* ★ Red Sole Love

www.sosuemelashes.com

How to...Apply False Lashes Like a Pro!

I love using DUO Adhesive whenever I am applying my SoSueMe Lashes. It dries clear, and it keeps your falsies firmly in place. In fact, this is the glue you will see most makeup artists using. Best of all, you only need a tiny amount of it, so it lasts ages.

If, however, you have trouble applying your strip lashes, then you will be pleased to hear that there is a way you can make the process so much easier.

Step 1 Place the lashes lightly over your eye – measure the lash to the length of your eye.

Step 2 After you have a rough idea – trim your lashes to fit your eye shape.

Step 3 Now, for the glue. You can apply the glue directly to the strip itself, however, if you find this a little tricky, then there is another way! Dab some glue onto the plastic tray your lashes come in, and then take the tip of a thin makeup brush handle, dip it into the glue, and run it along the strip of the lash! Doing this should prevent you from using too much glue.

Allow 15-20 seconds for the glue to dry and become tacky. If you stick the lashes on immediately after applying the glue, it will be very difficult to keep them in place. Allowing the glue a little time to dry first will make it the application process much easier.

Step 4 Next, place the strip onto the centre of your eye. Wait a few seconds for the glue to grip, then lightly press it down, inwards and outwards. Make sure to position it as close as possible to your natural lash line.

Step 5 To hide any trace of the lash strip or unevenness – always apply some eyeliner once the glue has dried. Duo is white in colour, but, you will know the glue is dry once all noticeable traces of white have disappeared.

SoSueMe's Handbag Must-Have: Balmi Lip Balm

If, like me, you have a lip balm obsession, then you are going to love Balmi Lip Balm (€5.95 /£4.99).

First thing's first, the packaging is uber-cool! The lip balm itself is shaped like a cute little ball and it's perfect for on-the-go application.

Best of all, there is also a small black chord attached to the product, so you can hook the lip balm to your phone, keys or maybe even your handbag!

The balm itself has a really nice texture, and doesn't feel at all greasy or sticky!

(I HATE sticky lip balms.) Balmi Lip Balm also glides smoothly over the lips, which means no more dipping your fingers into a small tube – a huge plus!

Its moisturising ingredients include antioxidant-rich Vitamin E, Shea Butter, and Jojoba Oil, all of which help leave your lips super soft and smooth. With an SPF of 15, the balm will also protect your lips from harmful UVA rays. Balmi Lip Balm comes in four flavours, but I particularly loved the raspberry and coconut flavours! Balmi Lip Balm is available from selected pharmacies around Ireland and the UK.

Celebrity Beauty Favourites: Skincare

I have hand picked a few of my favourite celebrities and I have looked into what skincare products are their favourite and why? Here is the low down…

Beyoncé

Queen Bey loves Aquafor Healing Ointment, which is also a beauty favourite of Kim Kardashian. This multi-purpose product can be used as an eye cream, a lip moisturiser, and, as an eye makeup remover. It's also particularly good for dry skin. Beyoncé has said in the past that she washes her face twice a day, sometimes more if she's working. Her favourite facial wash and moisturiser is by Natura Bissé; while her favourite exfoliant is by the brand Carol's Daughter. When it comes to fighting wrinkles, Beyoncé is a huge fan of using Dremu Oil. To keep her lips soft, she uses Smith's Rosebud Salve (menthol and eucalyptus flavour is her favourite). In terms of body products, Beyoncé loves Ivory Body Soap, and, Johnson's Baby Lotion. She also likes to use Johnson's Baby Oil whenever she wants to give her skin a nice sheen.

Blogger Tip!

If there is one thing that goes down well on a beauty blog it's CELEB secrets. Most girls out there, including myself, love to know what the celebs are using whether it be skincare products or a particular makeup brand.

39

Cindy Crawford

Skin specialist, Dr Jean Louis Sebagh has been treating supermodel Cindy Crawford for the past ten years, and together, they have created their own range of youth enhancing skincare products, called Meaningful Beauty, (which can be bought online). Dr Sebagh and Cindy also recently enhanced the line's best products, so as to ensure that they contain the most advanced formulations and up-to-date anti-aging ingredients.

Miranda Kerr

Miranda's skin is so fabulously flawless because she takes exceptional care of it. She avoids chemical-laden products, preferring instead to rely on the benefits of natural products. She particularly loves to use Rosehip Oil, and, according to Miranda herself, she was so impressed by the results of Rosehip Oil, that when she developed her own skincare range, Kora, it was one of the first products she included. When it comes to everyday makeup, Mrs Orlando Bloom likes to keep it as natural looking as possible. In fact, she is said to use little more than concealer, Un-Cover Up by RMS Beauty, along with some tinted moisturiser, Tinted Day Care Cream, from her own range, Kora. Miranda's favourite mascara is Lancôme's Paris L'Extreme Lengthening Mascara in Noir Stretch.

Cindy Crawford

Miranda Kerr

Sue's Skincare Routine!

Another topic I am asked about a lot is my skincare routine. Looking after your skin, particularly when you are young, is super important, and, if you don't put in the hard work now, you might regret it later. Actually scratch that, you WILL regret it! Unless, of course, you are one of the lucky ones who has flawless skin and ages perfectly, like your mom or granny – *sigh*. It really doesn't matter what age you are, it is never too late to begin a good skincare routine. You just need to find the one best suited to your skins needs.

I get hundreds of emails requesting tips on skincare, not to mention questions about my own skin care routine, which is why I have decided to finally unveil all my skin care secrets!

I will reveal my 'go to' products, my daily and nightly skin care routine, and, I will also touch on the different skin types and conditions, so that way, everyone is guaranteed to leave with a little tip or two.

As a beauty blogger, I do swap and change my products quite a bit. I am constantly reviewing different brands and trying out new things, however my staple list of faithful products, as outlined below, always remains the same.

① Cleansing

Every morning and evening, I double cleanse using Clarins Cleansing Milk.

Everyone knows that they should cleanse their skin twice a day, but, what most people don't realise is that a single cleanse is

> **Blogger Tip!**
> Your audience will grow if you write honestly and as yourself. SoSueMe is full of my personality and readers feel like they know me and are loyal to the blog because of this.

often not enough. In order to remove absolutely all traces of makeup, sun screen, and general excess oils, you should always double cleanse. This also ensures that you are beginning your skincare regime with a deep clean. I prefer to use a milk or cream cleanser because I tend to suffer from dehydrated skin, but, for those of you with an oilier, or, problematic skin type, I would recommend using a gel or wash cleanser.

Another cleanser I love is my Soap & Glory Peaches and Clean! This is a cleansing milk and it's great for removing makeup and impurities. It also smells amazing. Seriously, if you like the smell of peaches/mint, you will love this. The bottle is also super handy for bringing with you when travelling. I sometimes use this cleanser in the shower after a long day, and, once it has been rinsed off, my skin feels so velvety smooth and soft. The price is very reasonable too.

② Exfoliation

As soon as my skin is squeaky clean, I move onto the next most important step in my skincare routine – exfoliating. Once a week, I use NeoStrata Skin Active Exfoliating Wash. This product is designed as an anti-ageing cleanser, however, I like to use it as an exfoliator. It's very gentle, but at the same time, very effective for removing any dead skin cells, dirt, and excess oils. This kind of exfoliator is ideal for me, because I don't like to use anything too harsh that might strip my skin. NeoStrata Skin Active Exfoliating Wash will smooth the skin so that the texture is softer, and trust me, regular use of this product will leave your skin healthier and more refreshed.

If I have an event coming up, or, if my skin is lacking that 'glow', then I exfoliate every morning using Dermalogica's Daily Microfoliant. I swear by this product. It's one of the only exfoliants gentle enough to use on a daily basis.

③ Toner

I'm sure by now some of you are expecting me to move on to toner, but, to be honest, I don't use one! I have tried them, but I'm not a fan. Today, most dermatologists agree that toner isn't necessary. It's main purpose is to remove traces of makeup and residue from your cleanser, but a high-quality cleanser should rinse off easily with water alone. Furthermore, most toners are full of alcohol, which will actually dry out your skin! Some women like the fact that a toner leaves their face feeling tight and smooth, but really, that 'taut feeling' actually indicates dryness or dehydration, so I generally steer clear of toners.

④ Eye Cream

Such an important step! The eye area is one of the first places to show signs of ageing, so treat this area with great care. I always pat on a pea sized amount of eye cream prior to moisturising. Your morning eye product should contain antioxidants, SPF and moisturising humectants. I recently tried Thalgo's new Collagen Eye Roll-on. This eye cream is a gel that contains native marine collagen which moisturises, smoothes wrinkles and surface fine lines. I apply this every morning and evening to skin around the eyes, working from the inner to the outer corners of the eyes, then from the temples towards the brow bones. I have to say –

So Sue Me... Secret

Always apply your moisturiser last, but just before SPF! Creams usually contain more oil than water, so if you were to put your moisturiser on first, your lighter, water-based gels and serums (or whatever you use) won't provide any additional benefits. If you apply your face cream almost last, however, it will actually lock in your other products, thus boosting their efficiency.

it is amazing and what I love the most is the roller application is quite soothing on the eye – like an ice-cube effect from the 3 metal balls which combine a concentrate for anti-puffiness, anti-dark circle and smoothing active ingredients.

(5) Moisturise

One of the benefits of being a beauty blogger is getting to try out amazing new products almost every month, however, there is one moisturiser that I will forever love, and that's Clarins Hydra Clench Cream!

This moisturiser is so easily absorbed and it instantly hydrates the skin, but yet doesn't leave the skin feeling in any way greasy. It's also suitable for all skin types, and creates a smooth base before applying makeup.

(6) SPF

The essential final step in my daily skincare routine is SPF. This is something no one should be without. An SPF will not only provide a barrier against destructive sun rays, but also pollution, which is equally as harmful to the skin. The good news is that unlike the thick formulas of sunscreens in the past, there are plenty of new, thinner lotions available on the market today. I love the Thalgo Oxygen 3-defence Fluid SPF 15 which combats damage from pollution and UV rays, as well as evening out the complexion, and recharging the skin.

So Sue Me... Secret

Clarins Instant Eye Makeup Remover is AMAZING for removing strong, waterproof, eye makeup! Definitely my favourite.

I was fed up of waking on a Sunday morning after a night out, and wondering how on earth I could have panda eyes when I had spent the time removing my makeup before I went to bed. Ever since I started using my Clarins Instant Eye Makeup Remover, however, panda eyes have not been a problem.

This wonderful eye makeup remover is strong enough to quickly take away all traces of heavy eye makeup, yet soft enough to moisturise the skin and leave it feeling so smooth. Best of all, it completely removes all the residual glue from your fake lashes!

It's a bi-phase lotion, (which means you need to shake it before you use it), and I loved that it instantly removes all traces of my never budging eye makeup! I also liked that my eyes didn't feel greasy afterwards, just really moisturised. This extremely gentle, double formulated remover is also very suitable for those of you with sensitive eyes or contact lens.

Sue's Top Tips For Healthy Skin

1. **Resist the temptation to touch your face.**

   This is my most important tip. By just touching your face, you can immediately transfer nasty bacteria from your hands which can lead to spot break outs. If you have to touch your face, wash your hands thoroughly with soap and warm water, or, alternatively, use a face towel.

2. **Find out your skin type, and buy products to suit it.**

   Everyone has a skin type, and most will also have a skin condition. This is something people get mixed up about the whole time. Just because your face is tight, doesn't necessarily mean you have 'dry skin'. In fact, it could just mean that your skin is normal, but that your skin condition is dehydration. It is so important to find out your skin type, and what skin condition you are suffering from, e.g. dehydration, acne, sensitised or problematic (occasional spots). Once you know what you are dealing with, you can find the right products to help it.

3. **Never squeeze or pick your spots (no matter how tempting it is).**

   Firstly, it hurts. Secondly, you can be spreading the infection, and, finally, it may leave behind an ugly scar. It actually won't make your skin better, in fact, it will only make it worse! As hard as it may be, just stop!

4. **Exfoliate once a week.**

   Exfoliating is so important. In order to remove any dead skin cells and make way for the new lustrous canvas of silky skin growing underneath, then you need to remove the surface. Regular exfoliating also helps regenerate your skin and encourage new cell growth.

5. **Use a face mask once a week.**

   Face masks are great for giving your skin that extra boost it requires. Whether you are dehydrated, oily, or suffering from a breakout, face masks will help you combat that skin condition. There are plenty of face masks on the market today, from budget friendly prices right up to high end, but the truth is, they work. So invest in a face mask and give your skin that little TLC it requires. You would be amazed at how beneficial using a face-mask once a week is.

(6) **Stick to your routine**

It's important to stick to your skincare routine. If you are forever swapping and changing products, your skin won't recognise balance and this is where some problems, such as outbreaks and dryness, can set in.

(7) **Diet**

Having the best skincare regime in the world wont beat healthy eating for good skin! You can have all the creams from the world's best counters, but, if you don't eat well then you can forget it! Your daily diet has a tremendous impact on the health of your skin, and, ultimately, your entire body. I try to eat healthily on a daily basis, and I firmly believe a good diet really does keep my skin glowing!

So what are the important vitamins for the skin?

If you want to take care of your skin, then start upping your intake of vitamin C. There's a good reason why it's featured in numerous beauty creams. Vitamin C spurs on your body's production of collagen, a protein that forms the basic structure of your skin. When the collagen breaks down, it can leave your skin saggy, so, by consuming extra vitamin C foods, like, oranges, grapefruits, tomatoes, and cherries, you will help to tighten the skin and prevent wrinkles.

Here are just a few of the fruits and vegetables to include in your diet for healthier skin:

– Carrots
– Sweet potatoes
– Spinach
– Strawberries
– Oranges
– Tomatoes
– Kale
– Cherries
– Avocado

How To Find Out Your Skin Type

Knowing your skin type is super important in order to make the right decision about a particular skin care range or treatment which is suitable for your skin and not the girl next door! The initial type of skin you will have is genetically determined – meaning that you are born with it. That said – the health and beauty of your skin later in life largely depends on what you eat and how you take care of yourself. A popular Russian saying states that, after the age of 30, a woman looks the way she deserves. Gets you thinking, doesn't it? To always look great, the first step is to determine your skin type so that you can match it with the best recommended methods to improve your look and slow the dreaded aging process!

Normal Skin

Normal skin is smooth and supple to the touch with small or medium sized pores. It doesn't get too dry or too oily, and it only has the occasional blemish. Consider yourself lucky if this is you!

Dry Skin

If your skin feels very tight and is noticeably flaky in areas, then you have dry skin. Dry skin can look rough and bumpy, but it rarely gets oily. It can often be caused by lack of hydration or malnutrition.

Oily Skin

If your face is visibly shiny, and literally feels slightly greasy to the touch, then you have oily skin. Oily skin comes with large, noticeable pores, and is usually more prone to blemishes. The skin may be shiny too.

Combination Skin

This is the most common skin type. Combination skin brings with it a hint of just about every other skin type all rolled into one. If you have combination skin, then you probably tend to get oily around your nose, chin, and forehead area, but dry around your cheeks. The rest of your skin, meanwhile, is pretty normal. A lot of people have combination skin.

Sensitive Skin

If you burn easily and have reactions to certain cosmetics, then you have sensitive skin. Sensitive skin is very hard to deal with because it isn't as durable as other skin types. You have to thoroughly test products before risking a purchase.

Celebrity Beauty Favourites: Supermodel Glow

Once again – always great to know what the celebs are using! Here is an inside scoop on what makeup products my favourite celebs love the most and swear by!

> " I love the confidence makeup gives me. "
> Tyra Banks

Victoria's Secret Angel, Candice Swanepoel

Candice is said to love NARS Illuminator whenever she wants to give her skin a healthy glow. She once said, "I use illuminator a lot on my cheekbones. You can put it on your nose, and on the bow of your lips, I always think skin looks better if its glowing so that's a good trick". Candice also likes to spritz her skin with rose water. Candice is a huge fan of the Victoria's Secret range of cosmetics, and has often used the VS PRO Radiant FX Face Illuminator.

Victoria's Secret Angel, Adriana Lima

Adriana Lima likes to use the Shu Uemura range of make-up, and has done for years. Whenever she wants to go without a full face of makeup however, she instead mixes a little shimmer powder with her daily moisturiser and SPF and applies it to her face for that subtle glow. As one of the most famous VS angels, Adriana is, naturally, a regular user of the brand's cosmetics line.

Victoria Secret PRO Radiant FX Face Illuminator

SoSueMe's Handbag Must-H
Nuxe Huile Prodigieuse Gold

Whenever I'm heading out on the tiles, my nightly routine just isn
spritz of this bad boy!

Nuxe Huile Prodigieuse (or, dry oil spray, as it's also known) is a moisturising spray that makes my arms, shoulders, and legs, shimmer and glow… just like the celebs!

Not only do I love its beautiful almond and honey fragrance, the oil never rubs off on my clothes nor does it leave my skin feeling greasy.

Thanks to its small golden particles, your skin will glitter whenever you move. Nuxe Huile Prodigieuse Oil, which is suitable for all skin and hair types regardless of age, is definitely one of my favourite ways to accessorise a strapless dress!

I LOVE wearing my
Nuxe Huile Prodigieuse
on a night out

Blogger Tip! Whatever you blog about, it's important to remember that your first audience will probably be local so building up your popularity can involve something as simple as having useful local info. For SoSueMe, that means showcasing products that are available in Ireland or including euro pricing.

There are two parts to the whats-in-my-makeup-bag-section:

(1) Day time makeup.

(2) Night time makeup.

Sue's Daytime Makeup

There is nothing I enjoy more than rooting through my friends' makeup bags! If we are all getting dolled up together for a night out, we each have a nose through one another's makeup bags, and try out new stuff. I think that's why the feature, 'what's in my makeup bag', is so popular amongst bloggers and YouTubers!

Me and my girls!

Neck and temples – Clarins Splendours Summer Bronzing Compact

Face – Smashbox Halo Perfecting Powder

Foundation – Maybelline's Fit Me Foundation

Inner corner of eyes – Rimmel London Soft Kohl White Eyeliner Pencil

Forehead / around nose / chin / cupids bow – The Catrice Prime And Fine Highlighting Powder

Eyes – Urban Decay's Naked Palette 2

Eyelashes – L'Oreal Telescopic Mascara Carbon Black

Cheeks – Fuschia Blush #3

Neck and temples – Clarins Splendours Summer Bronzing Compact

Day time makeup

Girls like to know what other girls use and well, when the topic is makeup, I think nearly all of us are always interested.

During the day, I love a more pared-back look. I adore fresh, glowing skin and a girl who looks super natural looking! The celebs I admire the most for day makeup would be J-lo, Jessica Alba and Alessandra Ambrosio. Sometimes less really is more, and, for a day look, I think this motto is key! You will very rarely see me wearing a heavy eye shadow look during the day, or even a heavy lip colour, unless I am heading to an important event or a launch that requires so. Instead, you will see me wearing a natural look with highlighted cheeks, a warm skin tone, luscious lashes, defined brows, and a nude lip.

① Foundation

I am regularly asked what foundation I use, and although I try a lot of them (another perk of being a beauty blogger), there are two that remain firms faves of mine. For day wear, I love Maybelline's Fit Me Foundation, but when it comes to my night time look, I use Buff HD Foundation (which I will talk more about in the section on my night time makeup). I have always carried my day and night foundation in my makeup bag. That way, wherever I go, I know I am covered for both day and night, should we decide to head out somewhere at the last minute. Some ladies would see this as a pain in the bum, but others will totally understand why. My 'day' foundation is always a lighter tone, not as heavy – medium coverage and really dewy meaning it's quite moisturising. My night foundation, however, will have more coverage, a longer lasting effect, and, it will be a darker tone to match the false tan.

My Choice Of Day Foundation:
Maybelline Fit ME Foundation

First off, this foundation is available in a whopping twelve shades, with each one containing SPF 18. The one I have been wearing is the 220 honey/beige tone. This colour is the perfect match for my skin tone. If any of you are trying to get a clearer idea on what exact colour this is, I would usually be MAC Studio Fix NC32.

This foundation is thin in consistency, which makes it so easy to blend. The colour 220 covers most of the imperfections on my mug, and the coverage is somewhere between sheer and medium, but buildable, so for me it offers full coverage, should I opt for that. I love how lightweight it feels, almost as though I'm not wearing any makeup at all.

I adore the finish which isn't like any other foundation I've tried. I wouldn't say it is matte, but I wouldn't say it is dewy either. It gives a natural luminous finish, making you look like you're having a good skin day. It has a smooth application, and, in the end, you're left with a flawless, natural finish. That's the result I'm always after!

② Highlighter

My Choice: The Catrice Prime And Fine Highlighting Powder

I absolutely love highlighters! If there is anything you will see in abundance in my makeup drawers, it's powder and cream highlighters. I just love glowy, dewy skin, and I always ensure my skin has a glow. One thing that helps achieve this look, is a good quality highlighter. Highlighting really gives a new dimension to your face, especially when paired with a little contouring, which we've already discussed.

This is a wonderfully light powder that can be applied to help you achieve that glowy finish! A pink under-toned highlighter with a soft golden glow, it is barely visible when applied to the face, but the glow is still there, so it looks very natural. It can be used day or night. I like to apply this highlighter with a fan brush and using a light hand application. I just apply a little on top of my cheekbones and temples, as well as along the bridge of my nose, a small amount on my forehead, and lastly, on my Cupid's bow to emphasise my lips.

③ Concealer

My Choice: L'Oreal Perfect Match Concealer

This has to be one of the best concealers I have come across! Lots of USA bloggers and YouTubers I follow were always talking about how amazing this concealer was, and so, I decided I had to try it out for myself. In short, I loved it! True Match does EXACTLY what it promises, and, once you have correctly selected the colour best suited to your skin tone, it blends in perfectly. I use shade 5, 'sable sand', and I just love the coverage it gives to my under eye area! Its formula helps even out your skin tone, as well as cover imperfections, and conceal under eye circles. Another plus is that it contains Vitamin E and Pro-Vitamin B5 which helps nourish, strengthen, and revitalise skin cells.

④ Mascara

My Choice: L'Oreal Telescopic Mascara Carbon Black

For dramatically longer lashes, this mascara is amazing! I have always loved that doll look with my lashes. I don't know why, I just think it makes me more girlie looking. I have only recently started using this mascara, and I'm a confirmed fan!

⑤ Eye Liner

My Choice: Rimmel London Soft Kohl White Eyeliner Pencil

If there is anything I love, it's big bright eyes, and, the best way to achieve this is by using white eyeliner. Rimmel's Soft Kohl White Eyeliner Pencil is really easy to apply to the waterline, because it's naturally softer than regular eyeliners, so you don't get any of that dragging effect. It's also very creamy and gives a really white, lasting tone.

⑥ Eyeshadow

My Choice: Urban Decay's Naked Palette 2

This palette contains twelve amazing shades, ranging from pale to deep, matte to sparkly. This collection lets you achieve lots of neutral looks, as well as smoky dramatic eyes, and everything in between. I love this palette and it's the perfect size to bring with you when travelling.

⑦ Blusher

My Choice: Fuschia Blush #3

As some of you might know already, Fuschia is an Irish makeup range available online. I love, love, love some of their products and one blush I use for during the day is this rose tinted pigment.

⑧ Setting Powder

My Choice: Smashbox Halo Perfecting Powder

I never used to use a powder. I have always suffered with dehydrated skin, and I always felt that powders made my skin look even drier and slightly too matte. Then, I was introduced to the Smashbox Halo Perfecting Powder, and immediately, I was hooked. First of all, this powder comes in an ingenious package where you twist the top in a circular motion and it "shaves" the pressed powder underneath so that you can control the amount you want to bring to the top! It also turns the pressed power into a loose powder formula, making it easier to apply. I love that the powder is pigmented, so you get some extra coverage, and it never looks too dry on the skin. Result!

⑨ Bronzer

My Choice: Clarins Splendours Summer Bronzing Compact

This bronzer is a perfect touch of sun, and sets the tone for glowing summer skin with three sheer, sun-drenched, powders, in one chic compact. At the very heart, there is a tiny golden treasure that brings the dazzling look of sunshine to your skin – that GLOW! I love bronzers that give my skin a glowy/dewy look, and this bronzer definitely ticks those boxes for me! Ideal for both day time and night time.

⑩ Lippy

I always have both nude and pinky toned lipsticks in my day makeup bag. My two favourites are:

* Kardashian Beauty – Au Natural lipstick (Nude shade)
* Buff Makeup – Stripped lipstick (Pinky shade)

⑪ Gloss

Lip-glosses in shades of nude and pink, are also a must.

* Kardashian Beauty – 'Au Naturel Gloss' (comes with the lippy)
* MAC Dazzle gloss – 'Rags to Riches'

55

Night time makeup

Nose/cheekbones/forehead/chin – Crown Brush UK Concealer Palette

Foundation – Buff HD Foundation

Eyes:
– NYC Liquid Eye Liner (upper lash line)
– MAC Eye Kohl (lower lash line)
– L'Oreal Telescopic Mascara Carbon Black (lashes)

Eyeshadow:
– MAC / Urban Decay
– Crown Brush

Cheeks – Sleek Makeup Contour Kit

Face – Smashbox Halo Perfecting Powder

Neck – Tom Ford Bronzer

Sue's Night time Makeup

My night time weekend makeup tends to be a smoky, bronzed, and with lots of glow and colour! I always contour with concealers for night time for that extra face definition to ensure my skin has that flawless, celeb look. Celebrities who inspire my night time makeup include, Cheryl Cole, Kim Kardashian, J-Lo, and Nicole Scherzinger!

① Foundation

My Choice: Buff HD (available online at www.buffmakeup.com)

When looking for a liquid foundation that will mask redness, reduce pores, and, correct skin tone, a HD foundation will do an amazing job. Within a few minutes, your face looks perfectly fit for HD TV, and that's exactly what the BUFF HD foundation does. The consistency is a little thicker than your standard foundation, but, if you moisturise your skin well before applying it, there should be no caking. The BUFF HD Foundation has a medium-high coverage and really works at evening out the complexion. It also hides any redness, and reduces the obviousness of minor blemishes and freckles. In fact, it completely covers them. This foundation also contains wheat germ, which improves skin's elasticity and helps skin blemishes. It is ideal for even the most sensitive skin. It's not oily or heavy either, and it seems to 'set' on it's own without a powder. The finish is somewhere between semi matte and glowy, and best of all, it lasts all night! I love it!

② Highlighter

My Choice: Vani-T Crème Stick

I just LOVE this amazing highlighter / blush. It's an award winning multi-purpose creamy colour stick for eyes, cheeks, lips and body. Vani-T's Crème Stick also blends in really well, and it's a great product to use as part of your HAC-ing routine. It contains lashings of Shea Butter and Mother of Pearl powder, so you really do achieve that soft celebrity-style glow. The stick comes in a ray of colours, but I am using 'Desert' which is a golden, terracotta kind of colour! It instantly warms the face, and gives my skin a gorgeous lustre that lasts all night.

③ Concealer

My Choice: Crown Brush UK Concealer Palette

I use the Crown Brush UK Concealer Palette when it comes to perfecting my night time contouring and concealing. This is a great palette for camouflaging flaws, under eye circles, spider veins, blemishes, scars and even tattoos. This product is water resistant and can last all day/night. The only thing with this product is that you have to be very careful when applying it underneath the eye. If you apply it too close to the lower lash line, it can create some creases, so be sure to blend it in well and add your powder to set. I love that this palette has such variety in colours. It's very versatile you can mix and create the colours that you need. It is easy to apply, easy to blend, water resistant and offers a wide variety of shades. I recommend this product to everyone, my friends are all buying it.

④ Mascara

My Choice: L'Oreal Telescopic Mascara Carbon Black

Definitely one of the best mascaras on the market.

⑤ Eye Liner

My Choice Of Pencil Liner: MAC Eye Kohl

I love my black MAC eyeliner. It's super pigmented and lasts for ages. It glides on so easily, and it has become one of those products that I just cannot be without.

My Choice Of Liquid Liner: NYC Liquid Eye Liner

This is possibly one of the best liquid eye liners I have tried, and frankly, I'm not surprised that Megan Fox is also rumoured to be a huge fan of it. This liner dries quite fast and is very long-lasting. It also has a nice sized brush that gives you the control to create either an ultra fine line, or, a big dramatic one! If you are on the hunt for a new liquid liner, you should give this one a whirl! It's super affordable and I bet you'll love it.

⑥ Blusher

My Choice: Sleek Makeup Contour Kit

Sleek Makeup Contour Kit in 'light' has a FAB blush, highlighter, and bronzer all in one! It's literally the perfect trio for all. If I need a little something over my Vani-T Stick, then I just use this. The colours are all pigmented, and it allows you to create a perfectly contoured, highlighted, and blushed face in minutes. The contour powder is a smooth matte shade of dark tan, which doubles up as a bronzer, while the highlighting powder is a sparkling creamy beige that is perfect for using as a highbrow highlighter as well. The blush, meanwhile, is a lovely sparkling warm rose.

⑦ Eye Shadows

My Choice: Smoke It Out Palette

This palette is amazing and one that goes everywhere with me. Compact and versatile with 36 eyeshadow shades mainly consisting of both matte and summer colours. Ideally for a smokey eye look – my fave!

⑧ Bronzer

My Choice: Tom Ford Bronzer

Tom Ford Bronzer. This is the BEST bronzer out there by a mile. It is available in four colours, has amazing staying power, and the compact comes with a huge mirror. Admittedly, it's somewhat more expensive than other bronzers, but it will last you ages, so from that point of view, it does merit its price tag. As far as makeup products go, this one is a worthy investment.

⑨ Lippy

My favourite brands and shades:

★ Tom Ford: Pink Dusk (nude pink shade)
★ Tom Ford: True Coral (coral shade)
★ Tom Ford Flamingo: (bright pink shade)
★ No7 Love Red

★ Kate Moss: 03 (nude shade)
★ Kate Moss: 107 (berry shade)

⑩ Lashes

My Choice: SoSueMe Lashes

Of course I love all seven styles of this range. After all, I designed them, so they're my babies, and I'm very proud of them! But my two faves have to be:

★ **Red Carpet Glam**

I love this lash style! Full, long, glamorous and big, they remind me of the scene in *Aladdin* when Aladdin gets lost in Princess Jasmine's eyes!

★ **Champagne Kisses**

These are half lashes, and I love the extra flirty look they create, be it for day or night. They are perfect for any occasion. I always feel sexy wearing them as they really give that outer corner 'kick' to my lashes. Sometimes, when I wear my Red Carpet Glam lashes, I also add some Champagne Kisses lashes for that extra oomph at the outer edges. Love!

SoSueMe Lashes Coming Soon!

www.sosueme.ie

My choice of lash glue

Celebrity Makeup Routine: Kim Kardashian

Kim Kardashian is like Marmite – you either love or hate her… and I love her! First and foremost, in my opinion she is a very clever businesswoman – okay, let's try and forget about *that* hiccup she had at the start of her career, and, look at what she has accomplished since. Owning her own clothing/jewellery and perfume line – Kim Kardashian is a successful business lady. On top of that, in my eyes she is beautiful and I always LOVE her makeup looks! Her makeup style is so me – lots of contouring, bright eyes with a slight smokey effect and glowing skin! Because she is my fave celeb in the makeup stakes, I have looked into what her full makeup routine involves… and this is it:

Blogger Tip!

Readers appreciate passion! Sometimes it just comes down to writing about what you love (in my case - Kim K!) and happily that tends to be what you know most about!

Her prep

Kim begins her routine by using Kiehls Ultra Facial Moisturizer. To treat the skin underneath or eyes, she uses Aquaphor, which she also uses for treating blemishes or any patches of dry skin. After cleansing and moisturising her face, Kim dabs on some Intuit's Photo Shoot Makeup Primer, as she finds that this primer helps fill the pores as well as provide a long-lasting base for her foundation. She apparently loves using the Cle De Peau concealer stick in the shade Ocre, however she also likes to use concealers from MAC (in the shade NW25), or Makeup Forever. To combat dark circles underneath her eyes, she usually uses a MAC concealer.

The 'Kimmy' look.

Her foundation

Next, Kim applies Make Up Forever's HD Invisible Cover Liquid Foundation in two different shades. She mixes one pump of foundation shade no. 5 and two pumps of shade no 4. She has stated in the past that she uses shade number 3 during the winter when she is paler. Using a MAC 180 brush, Kim then blends foundations number 4 and 5 together to create the ideal colour for her skin tone. Another favourite foundation of Kim's is Giorgio Armani Foundation.

As I already mentioned earlier in the chapter, Kim is famous for her love of contouring. She likes to contour using foundation that is a shade or two darker than her usual foundation.

Once her foundation has been applied, she dusts on some MAC Select Sheer Pressed Powder (in the shade NC30, which she applies using a MAC 150 brush.)

Her bronzer, blusher, and highlighter

Kim is a loyal fan of NARS Highlighting Blush Powder, and is often spotted wearing the shade Albatross on her cheekbones. Her other preferred blushes however, are by MAC. She first uses a shade called Gingerly to warm up her skin, before then adding a rose colour called Cheek. She has said in the past that her favourite shade of MAC blush is Fabulush.

To lightly bronze her skin, Kim dusts on a MAC Powder (NW45). She is also a huge fan of the Smashbox bronzer, and sometimes uses this to further emphasise her contoured features.

Her eye makeup

A variety of products help Kim to create her famous smoky eyes. As an eyeshadow base, she uses MAC Paint Pot in the shade 'Bare Canvas', and she applies this base using a MAC 217 brush.

Like most women, Kim loves Urban Decay eyeshadows, and, of this range, she particularly likes to use the 'Vapor' shade on the inner corners of her eyes. While she is also a huge fan of the Make Up Forever eyeshadows, Kim's overall favourite eye colours appear to be from MAC, and she particularly enjoys using their colour cream pots.

The MAC shades she turns to, when creating specific looks, are:

★ Black smoky eye – Carbon.

★ Grey smoky eye – either Knight Divine, or, Print.

★ Brown smoky eye – Embark.

★ Shimmery eyes – Tan.

When defining her eyebrows, Kim will use either an eyebrow styling pencil from Smashbox, or MAC's 'Espresso' shade of eyeshadow. For lining her eyes, she will sometimes use MAC's Carbon eyeshadow on her lash line, however, her overall favourite liner is said to be Stila's pencil liner.

Lancôme's Hypnose Mascara is Kimmie's all time favourite, however, you will also find L'Oreal's Voluminous Mascara in her makeup bag, along with MAC's Zoom Mascara, which, she is said to "sometimes use". Sometimes Kim will apply two different mascaras for an extra dramatic look.

Her lips

When it comes to lip glosses, Kim most frequently wears the NARS brand, particularly the shade Turkish Delight. For lipsticks however, she loves MAC, her favourite shade apparently being, Angel.

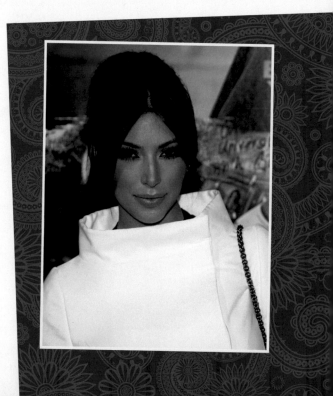

Whenever she steps out sporting her trademark matte nude lips, then you can be sure she is wearing a combination of MAC's subculture lip pencil, and, NAR's Belle De Jour sheer lipstick.

And finally...

To complete her routine, and polish off her camera-ready look, Kim dusts on some MAC Highlighting Powder.

Celebrity Beauty Favourites – Makeup Staples

> " I'm still the freaky kid who didn't do very well in school, who never went to college, who isn't always sure of what to say to people "
>
> Angelina Jolie

Rhianna

Rhianna's makeup artist uses foundations from the Iman Bowie range.

She also likes to dust on some MAC Iridescent Loose Powder in Golden Bronze, however she doesn't limit this to the face. Rhianna is said to love the sheen it adds to her skin, and so, she often has her makeup artist apply it all over. She also likes to use Benefit's Bathina Body So Fine as a highlighter for her face. Rhianna loves dark lipsticks, and her favourites include the Tom Ford range, particularly the shades of Bruised Plum and Cherry Lush. She also loves the Dior Addict range of lip colours, especially the shade, Red Desire. Rhianna's favourite gloss is Clarins Gloss Appeal in the shade Crystal. To keep her lipstick in place, she apparently loves to use Lipcote, which you can find in any pharmacy.

So Sue Me... Secret

SGC
SARAH.G.COSMETICS

Sarah G Cosmetics Face Kit Palette

Sarah G Cosmetics was founded in 2011 by Irish girl Sarah Grainger, who moved from Cork City to Glasgow in 2006 with very little money in her pocket, but big dreams in her head. Turning those dreams into a reality, Sarah has launched her very own cosmetic line consisting of high quality products, all of which deliver impeccable results.

The palette includes:

• Bronzer • Blusher • 4 eyeshadows (orange, brown, white base and salmon pink.)

The bronzer is fantastic for contouring while the pink sorbet brush gives a lovely luminosity to the cheeks. The eyeshadow colours are also very soft and pretty – I love the orangey tone for smoky eye looks!

Sarah G Cosmetics are available from www.sarahgcosmetics.com.

And This Brush Is For…

Most artists will admit that they are nothing without the tools of their trade. Investing in the right makeup brushes and tools will not only help you create a flawless makeup look, but you'll actually feel much better about yourself knowing your makeup is applied correctly.

Finding the right brushes can be hard, and, as a result, you guys have HIGHLY requested this section! As we all know, there are millions of different shapes and brands of brushes out there, making it difficult to know which ones you actually need and which should be left in a

Blogger Tip!

When you build up trust, your audience will be confident in your recommendations and even pass them on to friends.

makeup artist's case. You definitely don't need to have a drawer full of brushes in every shape and size out there in order to achieve a gorgeous makeup look. In fact, you only need a few essentials, and you can add to the pile as time goes on.

Before I get started, I just wanted to let you guys know that Crown Brushes are my fave! They are great quality and super affordable, unlike MAC brushes, which I think are just so pricey!

Invest in the right tools, and you will achieve the right results!

So here are the top seven brushes I recommend you get, and I will also give you my favourite choice from Crown for each type! Below that, are a few extra brushes that I also find quite useful to have in my collection.

Sue's Top Seven

(1) Powder Brush

My Choice: SS022 Crown Jumbo Powder (€19.99/£15.99)

This is a must-have brush for applying powder on the face. You will use less product than with a puff and a brush gives a more even, natural-looking finish.

(2) Blush Brush/Bronzer

My Choice: Crown Angle Contour Blush (€10.36/£8.75)

I loved angled blusher brushes because you get an easy application of blush. This type of brush is also great for contouring the cheekbones with powder.

(3) Eyeshadow Brush (Flat Stiff Brush)

My Choice: Crown Deluxe Round Chisel (€4.36/£3.49)

This brush is great for packing colour all over the eyelid. You can also use this type of brush to smudge colour for a nice smoky look.

(4) Eyeshadow Blending Brush

My Choice: Crown C139 Stiff Tapered Crease (€3.86/£3.09)

This is the one of the most important brushes you can have in your makeup case. This brush is specifically made for blending out colour, and it really gets into the crease of your eye.

(5) Eyeliner/Brow Brush

My Choice: Crown SS025 Syntho Brow Duo (€4.99/£3.99)

Obviously this bad boy is for brushing through your brows and for applying your powder to fill in the brow area. It's multi-purpose as it can also be used on your lash line for eyeliner.

(6) Pencil Brush

My Choice: Crown C222 Round Contour (€3.39/£3.39)

This is one of my MUST have brushes. The pencil brush is great for blending out harsh eyeliner, smudging eyeshadow under the lower lashes, or, creating a very defined outer V. Since the brushes are stiff, it picks up a nice amount of colour too. I use for this brush everyday as it works perfectly for any type of "smudged liner" look! This brush is also fantastic for applying colour under the lash line area.

(7) Foundation Brush

My Choice: Crown C406 Large Duo Fibre (€11.61/ £9.29)

I love the duo fibre brushes for foundation application. This particular brush helps create an even application, and feels ultra soft on the face.

It's wonderful for blending out your foundation.

And A Few Extra Favourites…

Stiff Dome Brush

When it comes applying colour into the crease area of the eyelid, and for strong crease definition, this brush is your guy! You can also use this brush to smudge eyeliner on top or lower lash line.

Soft Dome Brush

Ideal for blending eye shadow just under the brow bone! This brush is also great for blending concealer under the eye area.

Liner Brush

I love the bent tips liner brushes- it makes applying liner so much easier! This brush is mainly for applying a gel liner product.

Cheek Highlighter Brush

I love the duo fibre so you can stipple on colour (highlighter) and that way it wont look to packed on – it gives a nice light application.

Flat Foundation Brush

This is great for highlighting and contouring, but I wouldn't use this for applying foundation, as it can cause streaks.

How to...Clean Your Brushes

This is a question I get asked a lot, but cleaning your makeup brushes really is one of the easiest things to do, when you know how. We sometimes overlook cleaning our brushes, but it is far more important than you think. The brushes are a breeding ground for bacteria. Bacteria and natural oils are transferred back onto your face from your brush every time it comes in contact with your skin. This can cause spots. Dirty makeup brushes can also affect the colour of the product you are applying. All in all, it is best practise to clean them once a week.

Regular cleaning will help remove:

★ Old Makeup

★ Dirt

★ Dead skin cells

★ Bacteria

★ Oils

My favourite brush cleaner is Cinema Secrets and costs just €15, but there is no need to head out and buy the most expensive brush cleaner out there! Here is a simple way to get those tools nice and clean.

You will need: Baby shampoo, or anti-bacterial soap and a sponge.

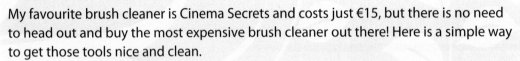

Sue's Step-by-Step...Brush Cleaner Guide

Step 1   Take a clean sponge and wet it using lukewarm water.

Step 2   Wet your brush making sure you saturate the brush completely.

Step 3   Squeeze a small amount of baby shampoo, or, anti-bacterial soap onto the sponge and swirl your brush on the sponge working up a good lather.

Step 4   Next rinse your brush with lukewarm water. You want to make sure you feel the brush when you are rinsing it to make sure you rinse all the shampoo or soap out of the brush. If it feels slippery or slimy, continue to rinse until your brush feels clean.

Step 5   Squeeze out the excess water and lay them flat on a clean towel to dry.

So Sue Me... Secret

Some brushes can feel stiff even after washing them, so to make your brushes feel soft and luxurious against your skin, take a small amount of conditioner into your hand and massage it gently into the bristles. Next, rinse in lukewarm water and lay flat to dry. This will give the bristles a soft, velvety feel to them. To help brushes keep their shape, very gently place a hair tie around the bristles. And there you have it! An easy and inexpensive way to make sure your makeup brushes are clean and well-protected.

CHAPTER FOUR

So Style Me

Before I get started on the fashion section, I want to say firstly that I am no fashion expert! I don't want this chapter to leave you feeling like you've just sat through a lecture, but rather, like you've just had a gossipy shopping trip with your best mate. I don't have all the answers, but, that said, I do feel like I know what looks good on most women.

What is fashion?

> " Style is a way to say who you are without having to speak. "
>
> Rachel Zoe

Fashion means different things to different people. It's an art, a business, a sneak peek into a personality. It's an escape, or a disguise; a tool of confidence. Ultimately, however, fashion is an individual statement of expression.

In my opinion, fashion is not just about wearing the trendiest clothes, but rather wearing something which makes you feel confident and comfortable within yourself. You know how they say that the first impression is the last impression? Well our clothes make the first impression for us. Even before speaking, we communicate with others through our clothes. The way we dress reflects a lot about our personality.

Back when I worked in the recruitment industry, the candidate's CV was the most important factor, but the way they dressed came a close second. Were they suited and booted? Did they look clean and professional? Let's face it, the individual who dresses well for an interview will leave a far better impression than the person who did not. Later in this chapter, I will take you through some style suggestions that would be appropriate for different occasions, be it a wedding, christening, graduation, 21st, etc.

Labels and trends aside, all that really matters when it comes to style is that you feel comfortable with yourself and your body shape.

Fashion content has been a big hit for SoSueMe. In this chapter, I'll take you through some of the topics that worked really well, with those all important Blogger Tips to tell you why!

Creating Your Perfect Wardrobe:
My 13 Wardrobe Staples!

 People will stare.
Make it worth their
while.

Harry Winston

Blogger Tip!

Even though trends come and go,
creating content around staple
wardrobe items and lasting fashions
will mean that you have articles that
don't date too quickly and people will
find the same info useful now and in
six months' time!

As the SoSueMe fan base
rapidly increases, so too do
the number of questions
I receive. So many of you
email me with your fashion
requests and dilemmas, but
one of the most frequent
questions I get, is, "What are
your 'fashion must haves',
Sue?" meaning, what do I
have in my wardrobe, no
matter what the occasion.

We all have those days
and nights where we stare
blankly into a wardrobe full
of clothes, while saying to
ourselves, "feck sake, I have
NOTHING to wear!"

Am I right? I do it myself!
What woman doesn't? What I
have found, however, is that
by having a number of staple
items to hand, I am now less
likely to have this melt down
every time I get dressed. So
why is this? Why don't you
have something to wear? The
answer is simple – you are
buying all the wrong clothes,
and you lack the basics.

The diagnosis: a dysfunctional wardrobe!

The medication: functional key pieces!

These functional key pieces will allow you to mix, match, and have the basics to create those simple, yet stylish outfits.

There are thirteen essential items that I feel absolutely comfortable in, and think are easy to combine. Obviously we don't need lists to dictate what we wear, but it's good to have key items that go with just about anything! This list can provide guidance for what pieces to invest in, as well as offer some structure in the way we shop.

Let's get started...

1 Black blazer

A black blazer is the number one staple for me – not only does it flatter all body types, it looks stylish and sophisticated matched with any other essential. Think VB here. Excellent for your 9-5, casual outfits, lunch dates and nights out.

2 Over-sized black bag

If, like me, you carry around everything except your kitchen sink, then invest in one of these bad boys! I love River Island and Zara for their over-sized black handbags.

3 Quality pair of designer jeans

I love the Victoria Beckham jeans, but Zara and Mango also carry an equally amazing range. They wash great and last forever. For a casual look, team your jeans with a blazer and a tee. For the 'going out' look, pair it with killer heels and an elegant top… maybe even a backless top? Fab!

73

④ Crisp white shirt

These days, I am loving those oversized, buttoned-up-to-the-neck shirts. They're so stylish, yet simple. Once accessorised right, you can wear it with almost anything!

⑥ Leather jacket

This is another item that can be teamed with everything. Think denim shorts, black tights, statement tee's and so on. You can also wear this little number with a dress, pleated skirt, etc. A leather jacket will give your look that extra edge, and it will never date!

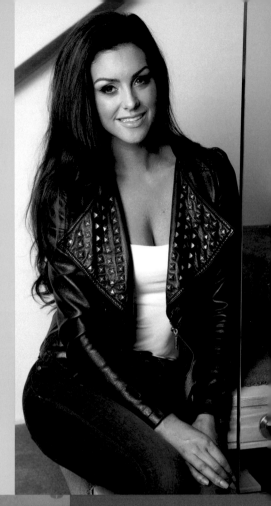

⑤ Leather trousers

These might not be a staple item of everyone's wardrobe, but, for me, leather trousers are one of the best pieces to use when you want to look effortlessly edgy in an instant, especially on those cold days. They'll rock with any of the tops on this list. Treat leather pants as if they were just your regular black jeans, and soon you'll start to see just how versatile they are!

⑦ The LBD (Little Black Dress!)

Every girl should have one of these. Your LBD never fails. Any style will suit, and you are bound to look super hot. My staple black dress is my leather one. I love it. LBD's are a brilliant basic that can be worn with virtually ANYTHING!

⑩ Trench coat

A trench coat is super stylish and NEVER dates. The classic belt tie is very flattering as it cinches your waist and displays your curvaceous figure. I'm a BIG lover of white worn with beige/nude heels. It's so sassy and stylish looking.

⑧ Levi cut-offs

These never go out of date! They're perfect for a beach holiday and absolutely all of the fashionistas have been pictured wearing them. You can also pair them with some black opaque tights for the winter.

⑪ Warm cardigan

This can be dressed up or down, depending on the situation. You can pair it with dresses, jeans, skirts, or dress pants, and it will always look perfect.

⑨ Printed scarf

A printed cotton/silk version should now be a key component of your wardrobe. I love my Alexander McQueen! Penney's also usually has a great selection of printed scarves.

12 Leather flat boot / ballet flats in a neutral or a versatile colour such as black or red.

If you are looking for comfort, sophistication, and practicality, then you will find them all in ballet flats or leather flat boots. They are really easy on the feet, while at the same time looking far more polished than runners or UGG boots.

13 Tank top

One of the most versatile items you can have in your wardrobe is a tank top. Invest in a white/black/cream tank top. They're so inexpensive, and they always look super stylish when worn with skinny jeans, high heels, and either a leather jacket or blazer.

One White Blazer – Three Very Different Looks!

> " What I'm always trying to say to the consumer is: buy less, choose well, make it last. "
>
> Vivienne Westwood

A Christening or wedding

Lunch with the girls

Night out on the tiles

> " Never wearing the same outfit twice and all that kind of stuff? Just a pain in the ass. "
>
> Jennifer Aniston

Creating Your Perfect Wardrobe: Making Space!

There is no such thing as too much space when it comes to a woman's wardrobe. A clean, well-organised wardrobe, as opposed to a pile of clothes, shoes, and accessories everywhere in your room, means you will maximize your dressing potential, and be able to create the most stylish outfits even on those hectic mornings. Of course, having the staple items in your wardrobe will also help in this regard. The task of de-cluttering your wardrobe can be overwhelming, so I'm here to offer you some organisational tips.

> " Be ruthless –
> you only use
> 20% of your
> clothes 80% of
> the time! "

Sue's Step-by-Step...Clear-out Guide

Step 1   **Remove.** To start, literally take everything out of your wardrobe and drawers (and wherever else you store clothes/accessories). Clean the wardrobe and drawers also so that you are putting your clothes back into a clean place.

Step 2   **Invest.** Invest in matching hangers and throw out those horrible wire ones! Clothes fall straight off and they look cheap! Opt for any other type, such as wood, plastic or satin covered! You will need three types of hangers: a padded jacket hanger, a t-shirt hanger, and, of course, a skirt/trousers hanger with the clippy thing on each side! Try your hardest to purchase matching hangers. This instantly makes your wardrobe look so much more organised.

Step 3   **Clear Out.** Start sorting through all the piles of clothes, shoes, and accessories, you've taken out (I do this in sections to avoid getting overwhelmed – it can be disheartening looking down at a big messy pile of clothes.)

Sort everything into three categories, and do a *Sex And The City* selection on it: 'Keep,' 'Maybe,' and 'Bin'. Most of these items will be anything that's be worn too much and beyond repair, too big/small, and items that are unflattering and make you feel miserable.

Step 4   **Time To Organise.** With the items you're 'definitely keeping', check that everything is clean and in good condition, and then start putting them back in your wardrobe neatly. Start by hanging items in categories and storing things where you can find them. I sort my wardrobe through hanging my clothes by type and then by colour. I then fold my jeans, and place my jumpers on shelves. Keep everything else in drawers, folded. No more just chucking them in and ironing them later, or worse, not ironing them at all! I stack all my shoes on the bottom two shelves of my wardrobe that my dad made, but there are some amazing shoe storage options from Ikea.

So Sue Me... Tip

When hanging your clothes, separate them in terms of colour, I.e. from light to dark. This will help you find specific items faster.

79

Step 5 **Sort.** Start sorting the two remaining piles, 'maybe', and, 'bin'. Go through the 'maybe' pile, piece by piece, and ask yourself, "Do I ever wear it? Do I love it? Does it honestly still fit my style/body shape? Do I feel good when I wear it?"

If the answer is 'no' to any of these questions, move it to the 'Bin' pile immediately. If anything needs to be altered / repaired or washed, do it that week.

Step 6 **Bin.** With the last pile, donate anything that is still in good condition to a charity shop, or, offer it to a family member/friend. Bin anything that has not withstood the test of time.

Step 7 **Maintain.**

You've now got everything in order, so try your best to keep it that way. By keeping a organised wardrobe, it really does takes the stress out of getting dressed each day.

Only put the items back in your wardrobe if they are clean, in good condition, and make you feel wonderful.

Looks You Loved

f 3,700 likes

What I Wore: Holiday Two Piece

60's Pin Up Style Two Piece: The VIP Room

Shoes: Korkys

One section that goes down a treat on SoSueMe is my 'What I Wore' posts. I myself love getting fashion inspiration from others, and I think this is why you guys love this type of blog post as well. I'm a high street chick through and through, here are some of your favourite looks from the blog.

f 2,982 likes

What I Wore: Holiday Outfit – Missee in Marbella

Dress: Missee.com

Bracelet: Missee.com

Shoes: The Shoe Rack

Watch: Guess

What I Wore: Orange Skort & Tee

Skort: Zara

Tee: Topshop

Shoes: Zara

Necklace: Penneys

Buckle Bracelet: MyMillyMoo

Bangle: Louis Vuitton

Watch: Guess

Neon Anklet: Taboo Jewellery

Ring: Coco Boutique

What I Wore: Leather Trousers, Neon Studded Shoes, & Blazer

Leather Trousers: Forever 21

Top: Irish designer Eamonn McGill

Blazer: Ollie & Mac Boutique

Shoes: Cari's Closet, Malahide

Watch: Guess

Bracelets: Alex & Ani

Bag: Cari's Closet, Malahide

What I Wore: Leather Shorts & Jack Daniels Tee!

Leather Shorts: Forever 21

Tee: FAB (in The Ilac Centre)

Leather Clutch: River Island

Watch: My new Juicy Couture Rose watch – love it!

Bracelets: From my own online SoSueMe Store

What I Wore: Berry Bodycon Midi Dress

Dress: ASOS

Clutch: Cari's Closet, Malahide

Belt: River Island

Shoes: iclothing.ie

I opted for no jewellery as I felt the dress spoke for itself.

What I Wore: Bandage Dress

Dress: Cari's Closet, Malahide

Shoes: Korkys

Bracelet and ring: Topshop

What I Wore: Denim Dress, Boho & Chanel

Dress: River Island

Chain: H&M

Shoes: Cari's Closet, Malahide

Bag: Chanel

Bangles: The Dress Pantry

What I Wore: Backless Dress By Scottish Designer Carolyn Baxter

Moonbeam dress: Carolyn Baxter (carolynbaxter.co.uk)

Bag: River Island

Shoes: Korkys

What I Wore: Long Sleeves & Sequins

Dress: Cari's Closet, Malahide

Red Sole Shoes: Cari's Closet, Malahide

Earrings and Bangles: Cari's Closet, Malahide

What I Wore: Red Leather Trousers & Tee

Trousers: Zara

Tee: Zara

Bag: Michael Kors

Belt: Missguided.co.uk

Boots: Givenchy

Jacket: Villa

Bracelet: MyMillyMoo.com

Hat: Chloe

Ring: MyMillyMoo.com

What I Wore: Black Skinnies, Wedge Runners & Blazer

Jeans: Topshop

Black Top: Savida

Jacket: River Island

Wedge Runners: Penneys

Necklace: Penneys

Ring: Penneys

Watch: Guess

8 Tips for Avoiding Dressing Room Dramas

① The 'Rule of Five'

When standing in a dressing room cubicle and trying to decide whether or not to buy a particular item, the most cost-effective solution is the 'rule of five'. Are there five other items in your wardrobe you can wear it with? Are there five upcoming occasions you can wear it to? Will you have worn it five times in the next five months? Are there five accessories you currently own that you can wear it with? If you can't answer yes to these, then it's likely you will not get your money's worth!

Blogger Tip!

List posts work really really well! People find huge chunks of text hard to digest, but give them the 'Top 8 This' or the '17 Best That' and they'll love it!

② Will it crease?

If the item you're trying on is silk, then creases are a given. What you need to do however is determine just how easily it will crease. To do this, just pinch the fabric for five seconds, and if the crease remains in place for more than ten seconds afterwards, then you can take it as an indication that the garment will be prone to heavy creasing whenever you so much as sit down in it. If you're not into high maintenance clothes, be sure to check for dry clean labels as well!

③ Timing

In many of the larger department stores, staff bring out new stock during the night, which means morning is the best time to bag the bargains. (At least early morning shopping also means you will avoid the dreaded dressing room queues!)

④ The small things

It doesn't matter if the item is a brand name or a budget name, you still need to run through the check-list. Does the zip slide up and down with ease? Will the fabric snag easily? Is the stitching completely intact? Watch out for stains and tears when trying on a sale item, as it is quite likely that a lot of people will have tried on that item before you. Be extra careful with patterned garments and prints as tears will be extra difficult to spot. If your garment has embellishments, make sure they are secure and not going to fall off in the wash!

⑤ Sale mentality

"It's on sale, I can't go wrong!"

We've all said those words when trying on an item in the dressing room, but I'm afraid the answer to it is: yes you can and will go wrong! Remember, if clothes are on sale, it's because people were not buying them to begin with. Some shops will even use a sale to try and get rid of stock left over from one or two years earlier. We have all bought the most ridiculous items 'because they're on sale', only to never wear them! Don't get carried away!

⑥ Mirror mirror

There are a small number of fashion chains that like to employ the tactic of flattery. You all know them! They have no mirror in the cubicle which means customers have to step out into the main floor of the dressing room to see what their outfit looks like. This is when the assistant swoops in to tell them how amazing they look. Don't let the assistant sway you. No matter how genuine her compliments might seem, never forget that she is paid to sell clothes, and may be working on commission.

(7) Go prepared

It sounds like common sense, but when you go clothes shopping, try to wear something that you can slip on and off with ease. This will save you time. A wrap dress, for instance, is ideal. If you don't have a tan on your legs, then wear tights. That way, if you try on a skirt or dress, you will see exactly how it will look if you decide to buy it and wear it out. Make an effort with your hair and make-up as well. No evening gown ever looked good with greasy hair.

www.sosueme.ie

(8) Navigate the shop floor

Is there anything more annoying than spending half an hour in the dressing room trying on item after item, only to suddenly spot a really stylish dress just as you're leaving the shop? Avoid this by developing a browsing routine. First, look at the clothes on the rails along the walls, then concentrate on the rails in the centre of the shop. Do it this way, and you will never again miss another hidden gem!

> " I'd love to have my breasts done. I wish I could have valves in the sides, so some days, I can have massive ones, and other days, smaller ones. "
> Sarah Harding, Girls Aloud

My Go-To Shops:

Online:

1. Missguided.co.uk
2. ASOS.com
3. Celebboutique.com
4. Boohoo.com
5. NastyGal.com
6. Choies.com
7. 9crowstreet.com
8. Etsy.com
9. Ebay.com
10. net-a-porter.com

Stores:

1. Zara
2. Forever 21
3. Bershka
4. Penneys/ Primark
5. Topshop
6. River Island
7. H&M
8. Brown Thomas
9. Victoria's Secret
10. Only

" I don't have a stylist. I pick all my own clothes. The best fashion is when you put your own spin on it. "

Mischa Barton

Dressing For ...

... Weddings

Rule #1 – never wear white to a wedding. It's just rude, and you don't want to draw negative attention to yourself from the get-go!

It is becoming increasingly popular to head off somewhere exotic to tie the knot, which, consequently, changes the staple wedding styled outfits! Tropical beaches are now a popular wedding destination of choice, allowing the ceremony to boast a bohemian look and feel. Long, fitted and heavy maxi dresses and fitted cocktail dresses are perfect for this type of wedding style. Think effortlessly chic.

For a city wedding, simple styles are key – sleek prints, bold colours, fitted cocktail dresses and peplum are on-trend examples of how to make a modern day statement.

For a country wedding, go vintage. Pretty knee length dresses are a key style. Floral prints and lace are also a perfect style for country weddings.

At a family wedding

90

… Club Night

Finally, a night to wind down and party, but what the heck are you going to wear? My rule of thumb is always, sexy, not slutty!

So, how do you look hot and draw the right attention to your assets without giving the wrong impression? Well, the answer is simple. Firstly, decide on which feature you want to show off. Pick either your legs, bootie, or cleavage. Showing off any one of these features is fine, but you don't want to show more than one, or you'll lessen the impact of your asset! I like my legs, so generally, I will wear a short dress that covers up a lot of my body, revealing my legs the most.

If you want to show your cleavage, then you can do this with a low cut top or dress. If your bootie is your asset, then go for a fitted body-con style of dress.

Hair and makeup are super important when it comes to achieving a glamorous look, so put your heated rollers in, lash up with SoSueMe Lashes and get your gloss on!

... Job Interview

Ok, appearance isn't everything, BUT (and there is a very big BUT here) when it comes to making a first impression with a potential future boss, appearance is certainly important.

According to a recent survey by careers website TheLadders.com, 37% of bosses say they have decided against hiring an applicant because of the way they dressed! It's no easy task knowing what to wear to a job interview, but, after my few years of working in the recruitment industry, here are my suggestions:

* ★ Solid colour, conservative, suit;
* ★ Coordinated blouse;
* ★ Moderate shoes;
* ★ Minimal jewellery – do NOT go in with clanking jewellery on;
* ★ Neat, professional hairstyle;
* ★ Tanned tights, or, opaque tights;
* ★ Sparse make-up and light perfume;
* ★ Manicured nails;
* ★ Fresh breath.

Neat and professional

... First Date

This is one question I get asked a lot from you guys! What is the best kind of outfit for a first date? It is so hard to answer that question with a blanket reply, because every date is different, but, if the date is just a light meet-up lunch or dinner, then, I would always go with fitted jeans, fitted-T, blazer, a high stiletto, and an oversized bag. I think classy is the way forward on a first date. Don't wear a tiny dress that reveals too much, it gives off the wrong impression. Go classy, it always wins hands down every time.

... Confirmation/Communion

When it comes to dressing for Communions and Confirmations, we can choose to be dressy or casual. In my opinion Communions/Confirmations are quite dressy. Mums, of course, love to dress up for this type of occasion and usually buy from their local boutiques which have matching outfits. The safest outfit I would suggest would be a day dress (cut just above the knee) with matching cardigan or jacket. Zara would always be my favourite got to shop for this type of event!

Blazer and fitted jeans

So Sue Me... Secret

As you all know, I love to wear bling (seriously, what girl doesn't?)

So it should come as no surprise to learn that one of my all time favourite online jewellery stores is none other than Crystals & Co, which is famous for its blingy accessories!

As you can see, my HerClutterBox is filled with their gorgeous diamante bangles!

www.crystalsandco.com

Vintage

" The sixties were a time when ordinary people could do extraordinary things. "

Twiggy

Why Invest In Real Vintage?

There are three main reasons why genuine vintage clothes make for a good investment.

(1) Vintage is so unique and as such, its unlikely you will find another person with the same item. You have to remember that there was no mass production when it came to fashion all those years ago. Most garments were intricately handmade, and as a result, its extremely unlikely that another one like it exists.

(2) When you buy vintage, you are essentially buying quality.

Think about it. The item has lasted this long not because of chance, but because of the craftsmanship behind it. The attention paid to every detail and embellishment is reflected in the longevity of the item.

(3) If cared for properly, the garment will increase in value. Auction rooms and serious collectors of vintage are always on the lookout for rare finds. Take care of your vintage and it may well reward you. For example, a 1925 Chanel cape sold for over $50,000 in a Paris auction house in 1996. Admittedly this was a rare record-breaking amount paid for just one vintage item however there is no denying that you could still get a decent price for your piece if you care for it properly.

Blogger Tip!

Remember that you don't need to wait for a press release to land in order to create content. Write about what you know and love and your passion will shine through for your readers. Vintage is one of the most interesting parts of fashion for me, so the follow articles worked really well on SoSueMe!

8 Tips for Buying Real Vintage

1. Don't be disheartened if your vintage piece doesn't have a designer label or any label for that matter. It wasn't unusual for women to remove the labels from designer garments so as to avoid paying duty at customs. As a result, many of the high quality vintage couture garments we have today are without their labels.

2. It is usually best to steer clear of garments that have stains or may be in need of major repairs. Firstly, there is no way of knowing how long the stain has been embedded in the fabric and as such, it may be incredibly difficult to remove. Secondly, the chemicals and heat used in the dry cleaning process may actually end up damaging the vintage fabric.

3. With regard to repairs, just remember it may prove very difficult to find fabric that matches the kind used in your vintage. It may also be tricky to find a seamstress with the skills necessary for repairing delicate vintage.

One of my fave vintage finds, a €25 blazer!

4. Know your measurements. When the garment was originally made, the average body size was a lot smaller. As a result, you will need to wear a bigger size when trying on vintage. Since many of the garments and dresses were designed to be worn with a corset underneath, it may be worthwhile wearing one as well.

5. Thoroughly investigate the garment. Gently stretch the fabric and check to see if the garment is weakening in parts. Above all, don't forget to check the stitching to see if it is all intact.

6. If you are buying vintage online, it is imperative that you know your exact measurements. The main areas to outline are the shoulders, bust, waist, and hips. Don't forget to allow for a little extra room so that you can move about comfortably.

7. Keep on the look out for vintage fashion auctions. Some of the larger and more established auction houses hold vintage haute couture auctions every few months, so if you're planning on travelling to somewhere like London or New York, check the web to see if there are any upcoming vintage auctions.

8. When shopping for vintage shoes, it's important to thoroughly examine the footwear before buying. Sometimes the seams may have weakened with age while the glue may have lost its adhesiveness. As a result, embellishments may not be very secure. Fortunately, most experienced cobblers will be able to repair and strengthen vintage shoes.

Creating The Vintage Look:
The Do's And Don'ts

Wearing vintage beautifully is a skill in itself. To do it right however, you need to know which techniques to avoid and which ones to embrace.

For some people, the term 'vintage' should only be applied to garments of a certain age, however 'vintage' can also be a 'look'. So regardless of whether you are wearing an heirloom, or an inexpensive sixties style dress that you found in a market, the rules for wearing vintage remain the same. Here are a list of tips to keep in mind when purchasing and playing with your vintage finds!

Centre your look around one statement piece

The main rule of thumb when wearing vintage is to avoid overkill. Simply take one dramatic statement piece, such as a dress or a cape and centre the rest of your look around it. Your vintage item is the statement piece, so make sure your other items and accessories are all low key.

This blazer, which I wore for drinks with my boyfriend, Dylan, is from my nanny's closet!

Accessorise & update!

Don't dismiss certain vintage garments simply because you don't like the look of them. Find ways in which the item can be customised to suit your own personal taste. Perhaps consider bringing it to a seamstress and having the shoulder pads removed, the waist taken in, or the hemline shortened. Maybe replace the buttons with pearl or diamanté ones. The outfit will look far better when paired with your own personal touch.

Know your vintage limit

If you want to embody a 70's look then learn from the mistakes of that generation and stay away from ill-fitting bell bottoms. Likewise, if you love the style of the Victorian or Regency era and want to recreate it in your wardrobe, then try subtle modern pieces such as lace embellished tops, or corsets, but don't go over-the-top. Remember rule number 1 – one statement piece only. What you want is to look elegant; what you don't want is to look like you are making your way to the film set of a period drama.

Mix & match for chic & unique

If you do own a genuine vintage piece, then pair it with something that is ultra modern, whether it be a vintage t-shirt worn with fitted jeans and a blazer, or a vintage dress worn with high heels and a shawl. The different items will compliment each other and add to the overall look. The advantage to mixing the old with the new is that you won't run the risk of your vintage garment appearing old-fashioned or dated. Instead you will look chic and unique. It's all about how you wear it.

So Sue Me... Secret

Tips & Tricks For Storing Vintage

Eliminating dusty odours

Beautiful vintage items have often been rescued from many an attic, however while attics might be a wonderful source of great finds, they also tend to be the home of dust and mothballs. To eliminate that dusty old smell, simply add a little over 120g of Bicarbonate of Soda to the washing machine's rinse cycle. This will leave the clothes free of that distinctively dusty stench.

Closet care

Always use padded unscented hangers when hanging up your vintage clothing. If the item is particularly heavy, fold it up or store it flat so as to prevent it from falling and tearing, When storing vintage clothing in drawers, line them with clean cotton. Remember, some vintage items may be quite weak, so never expose them to light.

Storing delicate fabrics

Treasured fabrics such as antique lace will damage easily if not cared for properly. To prolong their life, place a sheet of greaseproof paper between each item as this will help block any light as well as preventing the transfer of fabric dyes.

No more moth damage

If you want to store your clothes without the risk of moth holes, then place some pencil shavings in a mesh bag and use it as a sachet in your wardrobe and drawers. The shavings act as a moth repellent and your clothes will be free of moth holes when retrieved from storage.

CHAPTER FIVE

So Ask Me

Blogger Tip!
When you're starting out as a blogger it's important to respond to your mails and build up a relationship with your readers! Here are some of the most frequent questions I receive at SoSueMe

Wardrobe

Q I was just wondering where you purchased your leather shorts?

A I got them in Forever 21!

Q I was wondering if you could point me in the direction of an edgy looking black leather jacket. I have been looking out for one but I can't find a reasonably priced one for a poor student!

A leather jacket is so versatile it even works with geek glasses!

A I LOVE leather jackets, and I think every girl should have at least one! I would head to all the high-street stores. I have three – one is Lipsy, the second is Vila and the third is H&M. You can also pick up a nice one in Forever 21, Miss Selfridges, or Zara. Also, don't be afraid to spend a little on a leather jacket, it will last you a lifetime and leather never dates!

Q Have you any advice when it comes to wearing backless dresses/bodysuits without a bra? I love the backless look, but, I have a very small bust. How can I wear a backless dress or a deep v-necked bodysuit without looking totally flat-chested?

A I LOVE backless pieces, I think they are so elegant. If you are wearing a backless piece, then you need stick-on boobs! I got mine in Penneys and they're GREAT! Best thing ever! I think they were only like €5 or something, and I always use mine. Now for the V neck tops/dresses…

If you are wearing a deep V-Neck, there isn't a lot you can do here to create cleavage apart from highlighting and shading to create the illusion of bigger boobs (sorry lads – yes we really do this! Ha!) You can use makeup to create more pronounced cleavage. Apply dark shades to areas of your cleavage where shadows should fall, and light shades to areas of your bust that should be highlighted.

thomasmaher83, chrissypink, lyttlekate, studio716, petermulhall, ojbanks

How to... Create Fuller Cleavage

1. Select a dark bronzer or blush. Look for a bronzer one shade darker than your skin tone. This will create the illusion of shadows while still looking natural.

2. Apply the bronzer along the sides of your cleavage. Use a brush to avoid creating streaks. Brush on the bronzer, starting at the cleavage line and ending at the point where the strap of the bra meets the cup. Repeat for both sides. Apply the bronzer between your breasts. Blend it in with your natural skin tone, creating a "V"-shaped shadow in the process.

3. Select a light, natural colour eye shadow or face powder. Look for a powder one shade lighter than your natural skin tone. Apply the powder to the visible portion of your breasts using a brush! This highlights the roundness of the breast, giving it a fuller appearance.

4. Alternatively, select a shimmery glitter. Choose a body dust, lightly apply the glitter to the visible portion of your breasts. The glitter will create a fuller area!

Q HELP! I keep buying clothes I never wear! Any suggestions on how I can make the most of my wardrobe?

A Check out the section on 'Wardrobe Staples' in the chapter 'SoStyleMe'. Every girl should have her top 10 wardrobe staples, and, if you invest in yours, you will most definitely make the most of your wardrobe. You will never again have an UGH day!

Makeup and Beauty Products

Q What concealer would you suggest when it comes to hiding a bruise? I want to wear a dress at a family function, but the horrible bruise on my leg will ruin the look!

A Get a thick, cream-based concealer, not a fluid one, has to be cream! Get it one shade lighter than your skin tone. Apply lots of it, and after every coat – powder it! This should help hide the bruise. Dermablend Concealer is also amazing for disguising bruises, and is even strong enough to cover tattoos! A fast and easy option is a skin shield. Irish online store, SecretFashionFixes.ie, have a product called, 'Wundercover – Tattoo Cover & Skin Shields', and this should definitely help disguise the bruise. Wundercover's chameleon fabric sticks directly to the skin and blends in with most skin tones to camouflage areas that need disguising. (It's worth noting that Wundercover can also be used to protect your feet from blisters when breaking in new shoes!) For convenience, Wundercover comes on a perforated sheet for easy selection of the appropriate size.

Q I was hoping to get your expert advice about fake tan! I am looking for one that looks really golden and shimmery, just a gorgeous deep summer glow! Any recommendations?

A Without a doubt, Karora Instant! I swear by it! I used to always go for spray tans and now all I use is this. It's a lovely dark golden colour, it give off a fab shimmer/glow and it covers every blemish going! Here is a pic of me with Karora tan on.

Q I was flicking through your profile pics on the Facebook page and noticed your eyebrows! I have always been striving for the perfect eyebrows. How do you do yours and what do you use?

A When someone emails me about eyebrows, I always recommend going for the HD Brow Treatment. This treatment is brilliant. I would also suggest you buy the lash grow from Boots. Pop it on your brows twice a day, and it will help them grow.

Q I was just wondering if you could recommend a mascara? I'm using Max Factor- false lash effect at the moment, but it's not working as well as it used to. I have long eyelashes so I was just wondering if you've used any mascaras lately that you found were good?

A My fave two at the moment are Soap & Glory's Thick & Fast Mascara, and Eyeko!

The Soap & Glory one is really affordable and it makes your lashes thick and long! The good thing about this mascara too is that it has quite a chunky brush and I love chunky brushes because they put lots of product on the lashes. This mascara also lasts ages and it doesn't dry up as quick as the others! I would say give this a go. You can get this in Boots, and I think it's around €10.

Another mascara I tried and LOVED is the Eyeko Mascara from London! This mascara gives you doll-like lashes for BIG EYES. The multi-action brush with tiered bristle clusters is designed to plump, define and curl lashes.

Q I always think your skin looks flawless, what products do you use? I'm a student so I'm hoping you can suggest something while I'm on a budget?

A Thank you for your lovely comments! At the moment I am LOVING the new range by Boots – Botanics! Their products are really good and if you are after brighter skin (like I was) then this range is 100% for you! The moisturiser is only €7.69. Perfect for you or anyone on a budget! To find out what other products I love using, check out the chapter SoGlamMe.

Q My question is skin-related. On shows like X-factor all the girls' arms and bust areas look so polished, almost plastic looking, and I was wondering what is used on their skin to give that flawless finish?

A Well, first off, these celebs have beauty experts at their beck and call, so don't beat yourself up about it. To get nice polished looking skin, the key is a good exfoliation! Exfoliating at home is effective, but

sometimes you want to indulge in a professional treatment. In the same way a professional facial can leave your face glowing and fresh, a professional exfoliating treatment, or body polish, can leave your whole body smooth, soft, and vibrant. A body polish removes the surface layer of dead cells that can make your skin look dull or rough. The polish exposes the fresh, healthy skin. So I would suggest trying out a body polish in your local beauty salon. After this moisturise every day, even start using the Roger & Gallet Body Oil – I'm a massive fan.

After that, if you are heading out, always use a body glitter/light reflecting product – I love Benefit Hollywood glow! Its amazing for giving you that glowy polished look! Hope this helps! Enjoy your new polished look!

Q   As a new mom, it is hard to keep on top of the latest trends, etc but with your help, I still feel somewhat connected to the outside world! I wanted to ask you about supplements. After my baby was born, the hair around my hairline fell out. My hairdresser has suggested I try a supplement, but which one? I have looked around the web and cannot really find any reviews. I was just wondering if you have ever reviewed or used these products?

A   It's great to hear that SoSueMe keeps you on top with fashion trends, and congrats on your new bundle of joy! To be honest, I have never really 'reviewed' supplements as such and I don't want to tell you to try something and then it doesn't work for you, but I have been hearing GREAT reports about Tesco's Hair, Nail and Skin Multivitamins and Minerals. Apparently this stuff is amazing – your hair grows faster and even your lashes grow fuller. Your skin is left glowing and your nails strong. Every time I'm in Tesco's, this supplement is GONE… sold out! They get a new batch in every now and then, so if you can get in on time – stock up, it's also available online! For €4, you can't go wrong!

Q   I'm natural blonde – blue eyed and fair skinned. Would you be able to suggest any lipstick shades for me?

A   Right now, for blondes, I am loving coral and peachy tones! In general – blondes should look for lipstick shades as ripe as a piece of fruit in the sun. If your hair ranges from burnished gold to polished brass, look for apricot, peach, and even coral shades. Strong colours can be diluted by applying the lipstick lightly, blotting it, then slicking on a high gloss. This lessens the punch of the colour, and makes your lips look soft!

Blondes looking for a Twiggy effect may opt for a nude-lip look. Do not go lipstick-free, but instead, choose a lip liner and lipstick that are just a shade paler than your natural lip colour. Apply several layers, then top the colour with a heavy application of clear lip gloss. This look is regaining popularity and allows blondes to go more exotic on the eye make-up while keeping their lips plain. No matter your hair and skin tones, a rule of thumb is to go lighter if you have thin lips and to go darker if your lips are full.

Hair

As you all know, I do a bi-monthly Agony Aunt section on my blog, and the questions I get a 1000 times over are always about my hair. Questions such as: Where do I get my hair done, what extensions do I use, how do I keep my hair shiny, what products do I use, how do I style my hair, etc. Well today I am here to answer those questions for you guys.

Q   What extensions do you use?

A   A major part of my hair looking well is thanks to the AMAZING Great Lengths hair extensions & Ceira Lambert. Now, I've spoken about Great Lengths on my blog before, so I won't go into to much detail again – but basically they are the best. The quality, thickness, longevity and appearance is top notch! Celebs such as Cheryl Cole, Christina Aguilera, Jennifer Aniston, Tina O'Brien, Julia Roberts, Mischa Barton and even our very own Rosanna Davison love them!

Great Lengths Hair Extensions are worldwide. They have branches all over the world from Europe to Asia to Australia, which is very impressive! At least you know you're not going into some dodgy salon and having a lady who hasn't a clue how to apply your hair extensions, and leaves you with chewing gum bonds, ruined hair, and bald patches! *shudders*

Great Lengths have the best instructors/trainers and every aspiring GL extensionist must go through intensive Great Lengths training before they are certified and allowed near anyone's hair with the Great Lengths brand. You know you are guaranteed the best after they are trained here, and the best in Ireland is Miss Ceira Lambert.

Ceira's clients include, Rosanna Davison, Roz Purcell, Georgina Ahern Byrne, Georgia Salpa, and myself! For details of your nearest salon, visit www.greatlengthsireland.com.

Q   How do you style your hair? It is FAB! I have long hair like yours and the attempts I make at volumising it for a night out, are just so bad. I really need help with my hair.

A   Well, as I mentioned in my previous answer, I have the Great Lengths Extensions in, so having the thicker hair really helps when you are styling your hair for volume – but fear not! I can help you get BIG HAIR! First off, I use the Easy Sleep Rollers and I find them amazing. So many people were admiring my hair that I decided to order them myself.

How I... Style My Hair

How I style my hair:

★ Wash my hair
★ Pop in some moose while it's wet
★ Blow dry my hair using a powerful hairdryer and the big roundy brush
★ Pop in my easy sleep rollers
★ Sprinkle with some volumising powder
★ Spray with STONG hold hairspray
★ Blast with the hair-dryer
★ Sprinkle again with volumising powder
★ Leave the rollers in for at least 30 minutes. I always do my make-up while they're in.
★ Take them out, back-comb as you remove the roller, and pop in some Got2 Powered Volume Powder.

Q Where do you get your hair done?

A I get my hair done in Hession Salon, Drumcondra (they also have a branch in Clontarf) or Cowboys and Angels in Dublin 2. I love both salons - the staff are so friendly and up-to-date on styles, colours and cuts. I never leave either one feeling disappointed!

Q How do you keep your hair so shiny?

A I use all of the Great Lengths products. If you are going to splash out on high quality extensions, then really you should be using the 'hair extension' products too! A big mistake a lot of girls make is not using products developed for hair extensions and then what happens? The bonds loosen and you start losing your extensions. You have to be good with your aftercare when you have extensions and taking care of them is a huge part also. I get a new head of extensions every twenty weeks, and they always stay in great shape because I take care of them. I also get the odd mask into the ends of my hair when it's feeling a little dry. I think this keeps your hair looking shiny and healthy.

One of my fave products for shiny hair though has to be the Schwarzkopf Bonacure Oil Miracle Therapy Spray! For gorgeous shiny hair, all you need is a small amount of this leave-in oil spray, which will leave your hair feeling softer and sleeker in no time. I swear by it! This BC Bonacure Oil Miracle (liquid oil conditioner) has been formulated using precious Argan oil that boasts high anti-oxidant levels that help to fortify hair to leave it with a brilliant suppleness, softness and a gorgeous shine.

Diet & Exercise

Q Sue, what is your exercise routine?

A I was (and still am) training at least three times a week for an hour a time with my trainer, Brendan, in The Edge, Clontarf. My training programme is 'weight training', very little cardio, and a lot of weight lifting.

If you need gym motivation, think about getting in shape for holidays

In order to tone, Brendan explained that you need to first lose body fat and then build muscle. Women need to lift heavy, challenging weights just like men in order to gain muscle. While machines do provide sufficient stimulation to gain muscle, nothing can beat free-weight/ compound exercises.

Now, we will go over a few of the weight exercise that Bren has me doing in The Edge Clontarf. We call it the 'Curve Appeal—Exercises' to help add sexy curves.

1 Squats

Squats are perhaps the most effective exercise you can do for overall leg development. Squats are a great exercise that target the entire upper leg, quadriceps, hamstrings, and glutes. Like dead lifts, if you don't squat you are selling yourself short. These are a must for sexy, toned legs and a serious booty!

2 Lunges

Lunges are great for targeting the glutes, hamstrings, and quadriceps. Lunges will help tighten up your legs and butt and give you the curves you want.

3 Lat Pull-Down (machine)

Lat Pull-down work the muscles of the back, biceps, and forearms.

4 Dead lifts

Dead lifts are a full body exercise, meaning it stimulates just about every muscle in the body. Dead lifts hit the legs, back, traps, abs, obliques, etc. Dead lifts are a must for building a fully developed body. If you don't do them, you are selling your results short.

Q What is your daily diet?

A So the hardest part of all: eating right. When I started with The Edge, Clontarf, my body fat was 17% … now that isn't an alarming fat percentage at all, but, in order for me to tone and have the muscle definition I wanted, I needed to lose 4%.

I actually lost that 4% body fat in six weeks and gained 5lbs of lean muscle – result! So how did I do this?

Of course, I still enjoy my Eddie Rockets, Chinese takeaways, and Dominos, I'm only human after all! I just enjoy them in moderation. While you are training, you are allowed one cheat meal a week, and this meal can be anything you want. I always overindulge in my cheat meal! The secret is, don't let your cheat meal slip to a few days a week, or, you are just going to undo all the hard work you have put in!

So Sue Me... Secret

Being a model for many years, I have kind of grasped how to look 'okay' in pics at this stage, but, some of my friends and readers have asked me for some tips on how to appear thinner, or, just simply look better in pictures. It's not that they are necessarily unhappy with their bodies, but if you're going to be showing a picture to the world on Facebook or Instagram, then why wouldn't you want to look your very best?

So Sue Me... Tip

Photo Tip From The Olsen Twins
Whenever Mary Kate and Ashley Olsen need to achieve the perfect pout – without looking all duck faced – they apparently say the word 'prune'!

How to Pose for Photos

Girls always want to know how to pose, how to find their best angles, and all the things they try to teach you on *America's Next Top Model*. I'm no Tyra Banks, but, if you're in the same boat as my pals, then I've got some excellent tips that may help you look your best in pictures!

1 Know your best side – body and face!

Have you tried taking photos standing on the right side and also on the left side of someone? If you haven't – experiment with this! Most of us look better when photographed with our face/body angled toward the camera rather than straight on. I always stand to the right in photos and smile to the right because my right side is slightly more symmetrical and my face always looks better in pictures when I angle myself this way. So find your angle – pose in the mirror – it might sound vain, but once you get your angle right, you'll be a hell of a lot more confident in front of the camera!

2 No duck faces allowed!

Basically, don't make duck face in photos – it looks horrible, and it's never flattering! Everyone appreciates a great smile in life, and also in photos.

3 Twist Yourself

This is probably the most important tip! Positioning your body correctly is a great tip to look slimmer in pictures. You don't want to face the camera full on, because no matter what, that's going to make you look larger. Keep your spine straight and your shoulders back/squared, and twist yourself away from the lens. You can instead turn halfway to the side, put one foot in front of your other one, and keep that toe pointing toward the camera, while your weight rests on your other foot.

4 Watch your head

The position of your head actually makes a huge difference about how you look in a picture. You shouldn't pull your head back at an angle, for instance. That can make your chin look longer, so even if you're thin, your face will look much bigger. Instead, position your head bang on in the middle and slightly lift your head to elongate your neck.

5 Suck it in

This kind of goes without saying, except you've got to be careful about it. It's important, again, to have terrific posture when you do this, with your back and shoulders straight.

6 Watch the arms!

The way you position your arms is vital if you want to look slim in a photo. You can either hold them out from your sides just a little, so that your upper arms don't flatten, thereby looking wider, or you can turn three quarters away from the camera and put your hand on your hip. Not only will you look fierce, you'll look slimmer, too.

Enjoy the tips and remember – you should love your body no matter what its shape or size.

CHAPTER SIX

So Try It

So you've read all the tips and tricks and you want to try blogging for yourself? Well, I'm here to advise you on what to consider when you are setting up a blog for the first time, what steps to take when creating one, as well as sharing my own learning experiences with you.

This chapter will save you the time and heartache that I went through when I first started blogging back in 2010. In saying all that, I'm not an expert in any way, shape or form. I'm just someone who is passionate about blogging, beauty, and fashion and wants to share her experiences with like-minded people. As with any kind of advice you might hear, remember that your own personal intuition will teach you more than any other blogger out there.

First thing's first! Nothing worth having comes easy. You can't expect to be handed an internationally-read blog with over 400,000 monthly visitors on a plate. You have to work at it, and believe me, it isn't as glamorous, or as easy, as it seems. Yes, there are many exciting things that come with having a successful blog, such as going to plush VIP parties, getting free clothes, products, cars, and holidays. But on the flip side, the work is 24/7, and, if you don't have the specific set of characteristics that I am about to list below – stop now and forget it!

Most successful bloggers will possess these traits:

* ★ Hard working
* ★ Go-getter attitude
* ★ Determined
* ★ Consistent
* ★ Risk-taker

Good Reasons To Blog

To share your experiences – both good and bad – with others

When I first started SoSueMe, I was working in the media industry. I was also on the modelling scene, and so, with all the exposure to national and international celebs I was experiencing, I knew there was great potential for a blog that people would enjoy reading. For years I had wanted to work in media, and, when I finally got in, I still saw myself as a normal girl telling other normal girls like me just how it felt to work in the world of celebs, showbiz, and fashion.

Maybe your blog could centre around sharing what you do each day? Most fashion and beauty bloggers have amazing style, and while this is their primary selling point, you will also notice that they take readers through their everyday lives. That's precisely why their blogs are so successful! The reader engages with them on a greater level, and they almost feel like they have made a friend. If you blog consistently and build an honest, genuine, relationship with your readers, then they will in turn visit your site regularly to see what you wore or where you went.

To establish yourself as an expert and to market or promote your brand

Blogging is a wonderful platform that can help you to establish yourself as an expert in your specific field or topic. For example, if you're trying to get a job in a particular area, such as make up artistry, fashion styling, etc, then blogging can help legitimise your expertise as well as expand your online presence. Don't forget that blogging is also a wonderful way to help market or promote your brand or business.

To connect with like-minded people

One of my favourite things about blogging is that it brings together like-minded people. I have met some seriously amazing bloggers throughout my SoSueMe journey and we all share so many of the same interests. Blogging has such a vast community of people, and once you get to know your fellow bloggers, you can support and encourage each other.

To help and inspire people

Blogging not only changes your life, it can also change the life of the reader. The number of emails I receive from readers telling me that I have influenced their lives in a positive way is just incredible! SoSueMe has helped girls become more confident in themselves, inspired them on how to dress and taught them to reach for more in life. As a result some of them have gone on to apply for that job/position they have been eyeing up, joined a gym and achieved a certain fitness goal, or even set up blogs of their own.

Many blogs are also written specifically to help readers who may be going through a similar situation as the blogger. This is often the source of inspiration behind a lot of parenting, fitness, and health-related blogs.

Blogging means putting your time, energy, and world view into a piece of writing and then offering it for free to anybody who wants to read it. When others find inspiration in your writing, that is such a wonderful feeling.

Bad Reasons To Blog

When I receive an email from a young girl asking how she can start a blog because she wants an extravagant life where she too can buy designer pieces, be sent free products and become 'famous', my response is simple: Don't start a blog! Why? Read on!

Money

You should not start a blog to make money. If you start blogging with a view to replacing your full-time income, then forget about it. It doesn't work that way. Do you think that Bono started writing songs so he could supplement his income? No, he didn't! Rather, he did it for the love of it, and for the joy and fulfilment he received. The income came later, much later in fact.

Granted, the potential is there to make a full-time income from an established blog. I do it, Annette Haga of Nette Nestea does it, so does Chiara Ferragni of The Blonde Salad, and we're not the only ones either. The thing is, we all started our blogs because we loved fashion. We didn't set out to make money from it.

Internet fame

Don't expect to get 'internet famous' right away. Trust me, not every blog will grow as fast as SoSueMe did. I had an advantage because I was probably one of the first bloggers in Ireland to cover showbiz, fashion, and beauty all in one. It also helped that my blog had a memorable name.

At no point, however, did I aim to become well known through SoSueMe. That would have been ridiculous! My notoriety and quick rise to 'internet fame' as it were, came as a complete surprise to me, but it was most definitely the result of a little luck and a lot of hard, passionate, work. Yes, internet fame is very possible for you to achieve through a blog, however, if fame is the sole reason you are blogging, then you won't last. Eventually it will start to seem like a job, and if it feels like a job, then, chances are, you will quickly lose the passion and motivation required to continue.

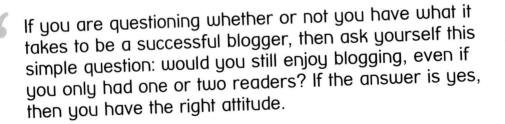

> If you are questioning whether or not you have what it takes to be a successful blogger, then ask yourself this simple question: would you still enjoy blogging, even if you only had one or two readers? If the answer is yes, then you have the right attitude.

How To Set Up A Blog

For those of you who are committed to becoming bloggers, this section will provide a light 'How To' guide on getting started.

Picking a Platform

Earlier in the book, I mentioned that I began blogging on Blogspot (also known as Blogger). This is a free blog publishing service that allows personal or multi-user blogs. I would strongly advise starting with a free platform, if you are testing the water within blogging land, and there are plenty to choose from.

A lot of hugely successful bloggers started out on free platforms. That's the great thing about blogging. Success is not reliant upon the tool you use, but rather how you use it!

If you eventually want your own domain, hosting space, and fancy website design, then wonderful, but be prepared, because that costs money and a fair amount too! It wasn't until I had developed a strong following on my Blogspot site that I borrowed some money from my nanny to build my own website!

For beginners, I would recommend starting off on either Blogspot or WordPress, and working upwards from there. The great thing about Blogspot and WordPress is that if you eventually want your own customised domain, they have the facilities to allow you change it (for a fee)!

Doing Your Research

Before you get started, I would strongly suggest that you read over the questions listed below, and decide exactly what approach you are going to adopt with your own blog. I would also recommend that you research your favourite blogs, and write down a list of reasons why you repeatedly visit them. If you are as specific as possible here, then it will help you when you get to work on your own site.

* Who is my target audience?
* What is my time commitment to my blog?
* How will I drive traffic to my blog?
* How often will I post?
* Will I include pictures/video/ podcasts, in my posts?

* How much personal information will I share with my readers?
* What will be the Unique Selling Point (USP) of my blog?
* What makes my blog different?
* What subject am I really passionate about?

Setting Up Your Blog

Once you have chosen the platform that's right for you, simply register a free account and follow the on-screen instructions. All of the major platforms are very simple to use, and will guide you through getting started.

Here are some things that are worth remembering which they may not tell you:

★ Pick a memorable name for your site and make it easy for people to find you online.

★ If you have social links such as a Twitter profile or Facebook page, include links to these on your homepage so that people can follow you and get regular updates when you have new posts.

★ You can also set up feeds from things like your Instagram or Pinterest account if you want to share photos.

★ Set up an 'About' page. When visitors read your post and like what they find, they might want to get in touch or simply know a bit more about the person behind the blog.

Choosing A Layout

Once you've decided on all the elements that you want to feature on your site, it's time to pick a layout that suits your needs.

This is where your prior research will come in very handy. What blog layouts did you like? Why exactly did you like them? What blog layouts did you not like? Were they confusing or hard to navigate? Learn from these flaws and make sure your own site doesn't contain them. Throughout the whole process, try to make your blog stand out, but, more importantly, make it easy and fun to read.

SO SUE ME

FASHION • BEAUTY • SHOWBIZ

Your First Post

Now all you need to do is write your first post. Maybe introduce yourself, explain why you wanted to start the blog, or even just share a story. This was my first post on SoSueMe…

I sometimes revisit this link just to remind myself of how far SoSueMe has come. I know, self praise is no praise, but every now and then, it's nice to look back and appreciate the success the site has enjoyed since those early days.

Once you've written your first post, it's time to promote yourself and start working on making your blog a success. The following tips, and my guide to social media at the end of the chapter, will help you with this.

Top Tips For Becoming A Successful Blogger

Find your niche

When I started, my USP (Unique Selling Point) was that I was a normal Irish girl writing about meeting big celebs every day, and becoming a fashionista on a budget. If you don't think you have a niche, then find one! Ask yourself what you are most passionate about, and why.

Ignore the haters

I receive a lot of negative comments and emails from people who aren't really my readers. These people are called seagulls: they fly in, shit on your blog, and fly away! I don't care about them because my site is not for them. If you get a hater on your blog, delete their comment, move on, and remember, for every one armchair critic, you have one hundred fans who love you.

That said, not all negative comments are bad. For example, if a comment offers some constructive criticism, then it might worth paying heed to their feedback. I'm not saying we should give validity to every negative comment posted, but some may be genuine and come from a place of concern, not jealousy. Those kind of comments deserve to be addressed, and perhaps it will help improve your blog in the long run.

Post when you're inspired

I really believe it is 100% best to post every day, and I try to plan my content that way, but there are some days when I'm really not inspired, or I feel like I don't have much to say. On those kind of days, it's okay to not post. Don't post crap – there is no point in posting for the sake of it.

Remember that you can't ALWAYS be perfect

My mam's motto has always been, "if you can't do something right, don't do it at all". It's a great lesson, but a hard one at that, because no one can ever achieve 100% perfection, 100% of the time. If, however, you quit before you have even started, all because you think it won't be 'perfect' or 'good enough', then you will fail for sure. A line I hear from a lot in emails is, "I'm worried I wont be good enough and what others will people think of me". If you have a negative frame of mind, you will fall at the first hurdle. Remember, things won't always work out the way you had planned. Maybe your blog doesn't look EXACTLY like you want it to, but that's okay. Just keep going, you'll get there!

Decide your own measure of success

Think about what it means to you to be successful and set specific goals to get there. Be inspired by what other bloggers have achieved, but don't use their benchmarks as your own – you are a different person and can follow a different path. The most important part is knowing what YOU want and figuring out how to get there.

> " Seagulls is my name for internet trolls. They fly in, shit on your blog, and fly away … "

> For blogging to work, you need to do it frequently and consistently, or the value of your site will evaporate. Aim to blog at least twice a week.

Know that you and your blog have value

Figure out what you're worth, and never sell yourself short. Do not do things for free! I've learned the hard way with this one!

Accept that it won't always be glamorous

Believe me it won't! There will be days when you will want to quit. You might feel like you're not getting anywhere with your blog. Listen to your gut instinct and take note of what is getting you down. I work 7 days a week, I'm constantly on social media and there are times when I get so run down, but I love what I do. So, remember why you first started your blog, and never lose sight of the fact that blogging isn't always going to be cupcakes and sponsorship deals!

Be genuine

This is the one of the most important lessons for bloggers to learn, I think you should always be honest and genuine. People can smell a rat, and do not think for one second that your reader is a fool, so treat them with respect.

Write the way you talk

I think this is so important, and it's how I write on my blog everyday. (Don't get too carried away with slang though, otherwise your readers might not be able to follow you.) Just stay true to your personality, and develop your own style, when you write.

Don't take yourself too seriously

What you're doing is important, and should be taken seriously, but don't let it get the better of you. When your blog is growing, it's hard not to get a bit carried away with all the excellent feedback, but remember why you started and stay focused!

Dedicate time

Blogging takes a lot of time, a lot of time! I could spend hours on the computer researching, checking and replying to emails or putting together a blog post/ review. If you want to be a success, give your blog the time it deserves.

Live your life

You're blogging about your life (or at least about certain aspects of your life), so it's important that you don't become so absorbed in your blog that you neglect other parts of your life. You still need to make time to enjoy yourself.

They are no shortcuts so keep going!

The most important thing you can decide to do for your blog is to keep going. Refuse to get discouraged when things don't happen as fast as you would like. Consistency is what will eventually set you apart. Be the blogger your readers can rely on, and you will win hands down. If you are looking for shortcuts, remember this: when things come easy, they go easy! Do the hard work of building your audience gradually and the people who genuinely enjoy what you're doing will stick with you.

Growing Your Blog

The simplest way to grow your blog is to post good, consistent content. By being honest and posting content that you're passionate about, readers will feel like they know you and relate to you. This is when they'll keep coming back for more! Once you've gotten into the swing of blogging and you're comfortable with your blog posts, here are my top tips on how to start expanding!

Marketing and PR

When you have established your blog and have a regular readership, don't be afraid to shout about it. If your blog is gaining a following on social media, chances are that brands will be coming to you, but if you need to give them a nudge to let them know where you are, do it!

Creating links with marketing and PR agencies can be really useful because you'll be able to write about new products and events before they're widely known about – always interesting for your readers! – get new ideas for content, and even get hold of some competition prizes to give away!

SEO

This is the 'science' bit. Most people use Google to find what they're looking for online. If you've ever wondered how Google decides what the first and second result and so on will be when a person does a search, well here's how! Google crawls the web looking for that search term and finds links to all the places where that term is mentioned, but it also takes note when people click on a link and how long they spend there. So – Google knows that if someone clicks on a link and then goes straight back to search within a few seconds that the link didn't have the info they wanted. In the same way, Google takes note if a person clicks on a link and then spends ages on that page – Google knows the info is good and moves you up the rankings.

SEO isn't quite as simple as all that – but it's a good basic explanation. It stands for Search Engine Optimisation and it means making sure that Google thinks your site is a good place to visit for info on your particular topic! Your first step is good content so that people will stay on the page! Next, remember to fill in the tags box when you're writing a post – these are the terms that you're highlight to the search engine and saying 'This post has info on these things, check out my page!'

You're also rewarded for things like updating regularly and being linked to from other reputable sites, so this comes back to having strong relationships with other bloggers, who might link to you on their sites when you have posts that they like!

Social Media

There are a multitude of reasons why every blog should have its own Facebook page and Twitter account.

Not only are they a great way to interact with your readers, but, on the days when you hit a case of writer's block, you can ask your readers directly what they would like you to write about. The biggest advantage to creating a Facebook page or Twitter account for your blog is the traffic that it can potentially generate. Every time you publish something new on your site, you can upload a link to its Facebook page and alert readers to the new content.

SoSueMe Tip... Five Benefits of Using Social Media

1. **Social media increases blog traffic**

   Whether you prefer to tweet or post a link on your Facebook page, this will hugely increase your traffic.

2. **Social media helps you create a personality for your blog**

   With social media you can create a likeable personality for your blog. I interact much more with my readers through my Facebook page than I do on my blog. After all, there are over one BILLION people on Facebook, so it is a relatively easy way to gather more readers. Big companies spend thousands of dollars on branding, but all you have to do is be yourself, post frequently, and respond to your readers online the best way you can.

3. **Social media makes it easier to generate a buzz**

   Social media gives you the chance to generate a buzz about something (and all for free too!) You can tease your readers with a competition, or an up-and-coming outfit post. Whatever it may be, social media is a ready-made platform that allows you to engage with your readers on a more frequent basis.

4. **Social media will bring you readers from all over the world**

   SoSueMe has readers all over the globe! The great thing about blogging is that you can write anywhere and you can read anywhere so your potential audience size is as many people with internet connections that there are on the planet! Social media helps to expand your audience beyond your county and even country.

5. **Social media helps you connect with businesses**

   Social media does more than just help you find readers. It can also help you connect with businesses, which can in turn lead to sponsorship deals. You have no idea what brand or business might be checking you out through your social media channels.

It's easy to become overwhelmed when the press releases and media enquires start rolling in. Take a deep breath and remember the following tips.

① Don't promise too much

Don't say you have 1000 readers every day if you have 100. Don't say you'll definitely write about something if you never will. If a product or item doesn't fit in with your blog or you're not a fan, just do what I do and don't talk about it. Ireland is too small a pond to be getting on the wrong side of PR agencies. If you like it, talk about it! If you don't like it – keep quiet and keep it off your blog. Nobody wants to read negativity anyway!

② Don't do too much for free

Nobody will turn down free publicity, so be prepared to start receiving press releases about everything from nail polish to nappy rash. You don't have to write about it all! Think of yourself like any magazine – be discerning about what you cover. What do you want to write about? What are your readers interested in?

③ Make the pitch!

If someone has launched something that you know is perfect for your readership or you have a great idea for a link between your brand and someone else's product or service, get in touch! Be prepared – know your stats, your demographic and what you can offer and make your case – the worst they can say is no.

④ Be honest with your readers

Treat your blog with the same gravity you would give to a magazine. If you get something for free or you are asked to review something, tell your readers. If you suddenly start expressing your undying love for a particular item and you have 50 of them – people will smell a rat! Your fans need to be able to trust you or they'll leave you, just like any relationship really!

⑤ Promote yourself!

Once you have an audience everyone will come knocking on your door wanting you to talk about their brand or product or event. Don't be afraid to push in the other direction! Talk about your brand. Promote yourself. Let people know when your coverage has a positive impact on what they're doing. It's not just about believing in yourself in front of marketeers either. Start getting your name out there by entering the Blog Awards, etc, and maybe even guest posting on bigger websites and the like.

Dealing With the Haters

Once you get popular, there will inevitably be those who begrudge you your success. I've had a tough time with this bunch. In fact, I was in two minds over whether or not to even include in this book, my experience with Facebook's infamous 'haters'. In the end, however, I felt it was necessary to highlight the other side of the blogging industry. While there are plenty of advantages to running your own blog, there is no denying that you do need to be prepared for some its disadvantages. After all, a blog can invite in as many critics as it does fans.

Before the SoSueMe Facebook page hit 30,000 likes, I didn't really have any haters per se. Granted, there would always be one or two readers who would say something silly, but there were never any nasty personal attacks. The negativity really only started after SoSueMe's Facebook page hit 50,000 likes. With such a large following, of course the page is going to attract hateful comments every now and then. It's practically a given for any Facebook page or blog with an extremely high readership.

DON'T GIVE UP JUST BECAUSE OF WHAT SOMEONE SAID. USE THAT AS MOTIVATION TO PUSH HARDER.

During the summer of 2013, however, I witnessed some of the nastiest comments ever made on my page. Given the volume of comments that are posted each day, most people probably assume I don't see everything that's written, but I do. I see absolutely every single remark that is made. When I posted photographs of outfits I was wearing on my holiday in Marbella, people started commenting on my figure, accusing me of not eating. Those remarks really stung, because the truth is, I love my food and have never starved myself.

In one of my holiday photos, I was pictured with Gaz from Geordie Shore.

As you can see in the picture, I'm wearing a bikini and a snapback cap. Amongst all the nice comments, there were some really nasty ones slating me, and accusing me of being "tacky like Tulisa". All because I was wearing a cap! It was incredibly petty.

In another holiday photo, I was wearing a backless top, which prompted one girl to snipe, "you could land a plane on your back, it's that broad". Another added, "do you even eat?" It was at this point, that some guy jumped in and told me to "go kill" myself. There are some haters who will use any excuse to criticise and insult you. I uploaded a picture of a top and described it as being red. Straight away, a hater was on informing me that the colour was coral, and that I was "a dope" for calling it red. They messaged me later and apologised, explaining that they had been through a bad day and had wrongfully taken it out on me.

I don't mind if someone has constructive criticism to make, and says something like, "I don't think those shoes work well with that outfit, maybe you could have tried sandals". Those comments are perfectly fine, but when someone gets personal, and says something like, "go kill yourself", well then I take issue!

I've had people accuse me of catering only for skinny girls. The reality is, I'm not catering for any one shape! I'm just showing MY outfits. Anyone of any shape can style their outfits to look like mine, if they want to. Another girl attacked me for even going on holiday. She wrote, "We don't all have your lavish lifestyle, where we can sip champagne, sit by a pool and drive an Audi. Think about us on the other side of the fence here". That message really angered

me, because I have worked so hard to create my own success. I haven't always had nice things!

Like I said, I worked long and hard to reach this level, and I'm proud of what I have created. The token characteristic amongst all internet trolls however, is that they want you to be miserable and down in the dumps like them. Some people might argue that bloggers leave themselves open to such hateful comments whenever they post pictures on Facebook, but I think that's just an extremely poor excuse to justify what is essentially a form of bullying.

Yes, I put myself out there to be judged, as do many other bloggers around the world, but that does not give internet trolls automatic approval to start spitting venom. Imagine uploading your holiday pictures to Facebook, and then having to endure comments like, "The state of that outfit, you look like you're going to a circus!", or, "The f****n' state of your hair! You'd think you could have done something with it today!"

Those are just two of some of the unnecessarily nasty comments I have received in the past, so before you jump to the defence of the people who wrote them, ask yourself if you would tolerate those remarks had they been left on your page?

Have some dignity in how you behave on social media. If you don't like an outfit someone is wearing, then either stay quiet, or make a suggestion as to what you think would suit them better. Constructive criticism is fine, but there is a very thin line between that and blatant hate.

Another nasty line I get thrown at me from time to time is, "You think you're better than us". No, I don't think I'm better than anyone, nor have I ever! I write about budget-friendly fashion and beauty products. I'm not head-to-toe in Prada every day, and have never once insinuated that I am. I do own a Michael Kors watch, a Chanel bag, and Christian Louboutin heels, but they're just treats for which I worked very hard and saved up.

While for every nasty comment, there are over a hundred amazing ones, it still hurts when a complete stranger tells you they want you to die. Fortunately, I was introduced to a very productive way in which to deal with haters.

One day, when I was in the Great Lengths Hair Salon having my extensions applied, Katie Jane Goldin, the CEO of Great Lengths, (and owner of the famous Paul Goldin Hypnotherapy Clinic)

When you're dealing with the haters you really need your friends around – both human and canine. This is my little buddy Coco!

Keep smiling and don't let the haters bring you down!

happened to ask me how I was coping with the haters. She had seen how bad the abuse had become on the SoSueMe Facebook page after I had uploaded my holiday pictures, and she was concerned about the effect it was having on me. I chatted to her about how some of the comments, and I admitted that they had even ruined one of my days on the trip because I was thinking about them so much. That's when Katie told me about a form of hypnotherapy I could undergo to help me deal with the issue more productively. She explained that a lot of people in the public eye, such as President Barack Obama, have used one-to-one hypnotherapy classes to help them deal with the pressures of their jobs, or, to help them conquer whatever it is that is causing them anxiety.

Hypnotherapy basically programmes the subconscious to cope with specific situations much more effectively, and the techniques you learn last a lifetime. The subconscious knows only what you tell it. If you have been telling yourself for twenty years that you are not confident enough to speak in front of a crowd, then that's what the subconscious believes. You have to almost 're-teach' it, and hone in on new, more productive, habits. That way, when a situation occurs, the same emotion is there but you deal with it differently. Once you re-channel your subconscious, you can deal with whatever it is that you are struggling with. My reason for undergoing hypnotherapy is to help me deal with situations such as haters, public speaking, etc. It's a tool of confidence, and, even though I have only undergone three of the required eight sessions so far, it has already helped immensely.

The process itself is very straightforward, and it has taught me a lot about how I react. Before hypnotherapy, I would have immediately fought fire with fire. If someone said something nasty to me, I would have hit back in self-defence. Hypnotherapy, however, has taught me that there is no point to issuing a temperamental reaction, because it says more about you, than it does about the person you're responding to.

THERE WILL BE HATERS, THERE WILL BE DOUBTERS, THERE WILL BE NON-BELIEVERS, AND THEN THERE WILL BE YOU, PROVING THEM WRONG.

If someone makes a nasty remark, I don't write back, or even entertain their comments, I just block them. There is no need for those kind of comments on any page, and there is no excuse for them either. If I don't like a Facebook photo, I just won't comment or click 'like'. If I think a girl should have worn black shoes with the red dress, then I would phrase my suggestion in a positive way. No way would I insult the girl, or stoop as low as personal jibes. I wouldn't dare make someone feel bad, and I certainly wouldn't dream of saying something that might make a girl overly self-conscious. I know what it's like to be on the receiving end of those comments. Sometimes I would find myself questioning my weight and worrying if I am perhaps too skinny. You become almost paranoid, but hypnotherapy has really helped me to stop taking things to heart.

You just have to learn how to deal with the haters, and realise that its not necessarily YOU they have a problem with. Testament to this, was a situation in which one girl left a particularly nasty comment on my page, thus prompting a number of fans to reply in my defence. A few hours later, she came back and apologised, explaining that she had just had a bad day and was venting.

The reality is that haters will always be an inevitable side effect to having a successful blog and putting yourself out there. If you are targeted, don't let it get to you. The nature of a person's comments will say more about them than you!

Onwards and Upwards

Over the past few years I have been lucky enough (and worked hard enough!) to see SoSueMe go from strength to strength. Hopefully the same will happen for you on your blogging journey, so here are my final tips for when you've put in the hard work and you're starting to see your readership grown and your website really take shape.

① Don't be afraid to try new things!

At the start it'll be all about figuring out what works – how much you want to share, what you want to write about, etc. But before you know it, you'll be used to your blogging routine and trying to keep things fresh, so don't be afraid to try new things to keep it interesting for both readers and yourself. For SoSueMe, this took the form of starting my own YouTube channel.

For MONTHS, you guys were asking me to start my own channel, and, when I made the decision to pursue it, I was honestly so nervous! Fortunately, the frayed nerves were worth it! Following it's first month in action, my channel had over 5,000 subscriptions and 71,000 video views! Thank you so much! It means a lot to me!

② Build your team!

You might get to a point where one blogger simply isn't enough! You have to be careful that you pick the right people to work with when it's time to expand your blogging team, but different people will have different strengths so being brave enough to open up your blog to a new contributor can be well worth it when they bring new skills on board.

③ Keep loving it

Whether you're hoping to build up to a point where advertising and sponsorship agreements will allow you to blog full time or you simply want to use the opportunity to meet like minds and get your thoughts out into the world on whatever subject you're passionate about, never let blogging become a chore. Be dedicated and take it seriously, but know when to take a break, know when to take a joke, and remember, it's only a little corner of the internet at the end of the day!

The SoSueMe YouTube Channel!

y

w

b

d

f

h

j

n

p

r

t

x2

HEARTWARMING MOMENTS

Over the next few pages you'll find some highlights from my SoSueMe.ie journey which I've mentioned throughout the book… that trip to meet Marc Jacobs, the Cosmo Blog Awards, and my friends!

Meeting Marc Jacobs

Everyone enjoys those surreal moments in life… moments that are just so incredible, you can't quite believe your luck that it's happening to you! Well, March 10th 2013 was when I experienced mine. After all, it's not every day Diet Coke jets you over to London to meet their new creative director, Marc Jacobs!

Two years of 24/7 blogging had lead to this amazing opportunity. In fact, the night before we were scheduled to go, I didn't sleep a wink with excitement at the thought of meeting such an iconic designer. I remember lying there, with butterflies in my tummy, thinking, "it doesn't get much better that this"!

To be honest, I was equally as nervous as I was ecstatic. I didn't really know what to expect, and, the idea of attending a press conference and red carpet event in London, where all the big interviews and launches happen, while sitting amongst some of Europe's leading publications, had me a little on edge. The event we were to attend was none other than the uber-glitzy 'Sparkling

Meeting the man of the night, Marc Jacobs!

Together For 30 Years Collection, With Marc Jacobs', in celebration of Diet Coke's 30th anniversary. Of course, I have been dreaming about something like this happening for so long, but, when the opportunity is right there in front of you, and you know you're about to experience it first hand, well it can be a little daunting to say the least.

Our day didn't get off to a smooth start! We arrived at Dublin Airport at around 8.30am, but the cold icy weather had left the runway completely frozen over, thus causing a three hour delay. Diet Coke was filming the whole journey, so we got started on that, while we waited in the hope that our flight would not be cancelled. Eventually, we were in the air and on our way! The plan, initially, was to drop the bags off at the hotel in London and casually head to the conference, but, unfortunately, because of the delay, the moment we left the plane, we rushed straight to the press conference in the hope that we would make it on time. Luckily, we got there just as Marc was about to step on stage (phew!) There was a small audience of select press waiting patiently for him at the German Gymnasium, near King's Cross in London – a beacon of warmth and excitement in the ridiculously cold weather.

They say you should never meet your heroes. This doesn't apply to Marc Jacobs. In fact, if you meet him, you will love him even more afterwards! For a long time, I was (and still am) a huge Marc Jacobs fan, and, when I met him in person, he was everything I expected and more.

Charming an audience of journalists at a press conference is not easy, but Marc worked the room like a pro. He has an amazing sense of humour and didn't take himself too seriously, which I loved. He joked that the reason he decided to work with Diet Coke was because, "I like attention!". He then went on to joke that he Googles himself "just to find out what I was doing last night!", and that he was totally fine about being a Diet Coke hunk because "I'll take my clothes off if anybody asks me".

Jacobs went on to explain how each bottle represented one of the three different decades that Diet Coke has been in fashion. A big shouldered, androgynous look was created for the 80s, while a full-on, hot pink glamour look represented the 90s. Meanwhile, an "eclectic, anything goes" finding-your-individuality attitude summed up the 00s.

Asked how the industry had changed since he started out, Jacobs said "the visibility was greater, the want for fashion has become so big". As a designer who likes to "live in the now" and is "not interested in having my clothes in a museum", he has embraced change in the industry, including the rise of fashion bloggers. "They're part of life now," he says. He also stressed how it was a good thing that fashion has become less exclusive, saying, "I think it's an old-fashioned notion that fashion needs to be exclusive. At Marc Jacobs we like to do low price, honest products like key rings as well as high end – it's more modern to think you can do both ends of the spectrum".

What struck me the most about Jacobs is his lack of interest in red carpets events, and, I suppose he has a valid point. "The red carpet doesn't interest me, because people have become all the same. I long for the days of Cher turning up in something transparent! The red carpet has led to a sea of sameness in Hollywood," he says.

When asked about who he believes are the most memorable females in fashion, he replied, "Kate Moss for me is very iconic – as a girl, model and as a friend, but also Sophia Coppola – her creative voice has been very inspiring to me".

Following the press conference, it was back to the hotel to get ready for the glitzy red carpet affair later that night. We arrived at 8pm to a sea of photographers all snapping away – it was mind blowing! Celebs such as Tyson Beckford and Brix Smith strolled in and mingled with the crowd, I was in awe! Guests caught a glimpse of the new limited-edition collection of bottles and also watched the Marc Jacobs ad. It was so much fun to watch. I was really impressed by it. The entire event was mind-blowingly amazing, and, definitely one I will never forget!

Friends

Friends are everything, and while making friends may be easy, finding true and loyal friends who provide a lasting and fulfilling friendship is a much greater challenge!

So what is a friend?

To me, a friend is someone who is there for you no matter what. A friend is willing to listen and offer advice, when needed. A friend will laugh and cry with you. A friend is kind, loving and trustworthy! A friend won't judge you. A friend will like you for who you are and accept you for who you are – but a friend will also pull you up on something, if needs be. A friend won't try to change you. A friend will forgive if you both have a silly argument. A friend will love you and stay by your side when everyone else walks out. A friend will support you and encourage you through every step of the way, no matter how big or small a dream may be.

I am lucky to have the best friends in the world and I can safely say that I have the best friends anyone can ask for! I don't get to see my friends every week, I have a very busy working schedule, but – the thing I love the most about my friends is – it doesn't matter if we haven't spoken in a week or sometimes two weeks, I know as soon as I pick up the phone to them it's like we never left off!

Love you guys!

xx

2010/09/24

The Cosmo Blog Awards

What I Wore...

Fitted Tartan Pants: Bershka
Shirt: Zara
Blazer: Bershka
Neck Scarf: Miss Selfridges
Shoes: Penneys
Bag: Chanel

October 2013 marked the fourth Cosmo Blog Awards in association with Next, which were held at the ultra-glamorous OXO2 Tower in London city! SoSueMe was nominated in two categories – Best Blog and Best International Fashion Blog – which was a super achievement and I was so proud!

I suppose, being a fashion blogger, you would think I had been planning my outfit for weeks and my suitcase was full to the brim, right? Well quite the opposite in fact! I had nothing in it but shoes, makeup and accessories. I had walked all of Dublin one of the days prior to the event looking for an outfit and I didn't see one thing that caught me eye! From the word go, I had the tartan trend in mind, I just adore it at the minute. I didn't want to go with the cliché dress – I wanted to be different – so I had a preppy suit in mind and I was on the hunt to find it once I got to London.

Of course – lo and behold, the first shop I went into on Oxford Street – I found a big chunk of outfit! London is SO AMAZING for shopping and going to an awards show steeped in magazine and fashion types meant an ultimate What I Wore moment for SoSueMe – it had to be perfect.

It's only when you're finally in the room, surrounded by the other top people in your industry all gathered to celebrate what you do, that you can really take a moment to think about all you've achieved. This was definitely another highlight on the SoSueMe journey and it leaves me with one piece of advice for when you start reaching your goals – whether blogging or anything else – take time to appreciate how far you've come!

To my pals – you know who you all are!

Thank you for your continued support, love and the encouragement you show me each day! Thank you for supporting me throughout my SoSueMe.ie journey. Thank you for keeping me grounded, thank you for listening to me when I needed a rant and most of all, thank you for always being there, no matter what!

I love each and every one of you!

Dylan – my best friend and boyfriend, you are the most caring person I have ever met! I grow in love with you more and more everyday! Thank you for always being there. You're my rock. I love you!

Sue xx

> " Be nice in what you say to people. Don't begrudge them their successes and don't be happy for their failures. Be complimentary, not critical. Remember, even those who appear to be in the brightest of moods can have the darkest of problems. Don't be the reason someone has a bad day… be the reason they have a great day. Be happy, be positive, and good things will come. "

Thanks!